Picosecond Chemistry and Biology

T. A. M. Doust and M. A. West

*Based on the Proceedings of a Symposium
held at the Royal Institution, London*

Science Reviews Limited

7120 - 2870

ISBN 0-905927-36-2

Science Reviews Ltd.
40 The Fairway
Northwood, Middlesex, HA6 3DY
England.

Printed in Great Britain by Antony Rowe Ltd., Chippenham
and bound by Green Street Bindery, Oxford

Contents

Preface

There is considerable interest in the study of primary
photo-induced primary events in chemistry and biology
largely due to the environmental sensitivity of the
relaxation dynamics. The experimental problems of
picosecond spectroscopy lie both in the production of
optical pulses at suitable wavelengths and in detection
apparatus. Current European research in picosecond
spectroscopy was outlined in a series of talks and posters
given in a meeting entitled *Picosecond Chemistry and
Biology* held at the Royal Institution in November 1982.

Studies of real-time events were discussed by Taylor
who described new developments in synchronously-scanning
streak cameras capable of 1 ps resolution. In conjunction
with a frequency-doubled CW mode-locked dye laser, this
overall system was used to examine the kinetics of
potential saturable absorbing species throughout the
visible region. Doust described the technique of *up-
conversion* - one of the few allowing sensitive measurements
on short-lived fluorophors in the red and infrared.
Measurement of rotational diffusion rates of a dye in mixed
solvent systems is one representative application of the
technique. Recent progress in amplifying ultrashort
pulses was reviewed by Ferguson. He described the use of
amplified dye laser pulses to generate a broadband
continuum of subpicosecond duration. This type of pulse

has been used for multiwavelength picosecond absorption
spectroscopy. Reekie and coworkers discussed the
production of mode locked pulses in the infrared at
2.7 μm by synchronously pumping a colour centre laser.
If a mode-locked CW dye laser is used for pumping, it
is reported that two tunable synchronised pulse trains
are available.

Sundstrom and coworkers described the use of a time
resolved absorption technique in the study of
conformational dynamics in the ground and electronically
excited states of cyanine and triphenylmethane molecules.
Similar molecular systems were studies with a streak
camera by Winkworth. Pronounced differences were found
in the viscosity-dependent behaviour between diol and
monol solvents.

Attempts at using conventional flashlamp techniques
for picosecond studies were described by Birch and Imhof.
Nanosecond flashlamps have limited repetition rates and
produce pulses of low intensity compared with a laser.
Nevertheless it is claimed that, under favourable
circumstances at least, subnanosecond fluorescence
lifetimes of strong fluorophors can be measured. This
paper clearly demonstrates the limitations of flashlamps
especially for resolving non-exponential decays. On
the other hand, Stubbs and coworkers derived time-resolved

anisotropy decays of various DPH derivatives to yield
information on the motional properties of different
regions of the hydrocarbon region of biological membranes.
Recent improvements in detector speed have allowed the
use of mode-locked lasers with time-correlated single
photon counting to record and analyse decays as short as
a few tens of picoseconds. The papers by Holzwarth and
Chewter and coworkers both demonstrate how this versatile
technique can be used for the analysis of complex decay
kinetics including up to four exponential components.
This same technique was applied by Searle and coworkers
to studies of isolated chlorophyll-proteins. The
photosystem I reaction centre protein was shown to have
a major 40 ps component, indicating efficient photochemical quenching.

The appended bibliography covers some of the more
recent publcations in this subject and emphasis has been
given to applications in chemistry and biology. This
bibliography should provide a starting point for those
research workers and students considering entering the
'picosecond club'.

We acknowledge the administrative help of Miss Judith
Wright in organising the meeting and financial support
from Applied Photophysics Limited.

Thomas A.M. Doust
Michael A. West

Picosecond Chemistry and Biology

Introduction by Sir George Porter

Picosecond chemistry and biology have existed as long as
chemistry and biology but only over the last decade has it
been possible to observe these events in real time. The
techniques which have made this possible are the culmination
of developments in pulse excitation techniques which have
taken place mainly since the second world war, although the
principle has a much longer history, dating back at least
to the phosphoroscope (1859) of Edmond Becquerel (father of
Henri Becquerel), which had a time resolution of about 200
microseconds.

Only when a single particle is observable over a period
of time, as in nuclear physics, can time resolved experiments
be made without the necessity of some form of synchronising
pulse which initiates the rapid process to be investigated
in many particles simultaneously. The pulse may be the
injection of another substance (mixing) of heat (temperature
jump) or other perturbing parameters such as pressure,
electric field etc. Light, the first to be used, has however
turned out to be not only the most powerful and versatile
form of initiation but the only method which can provide
sub-picosecond time resolution.

The first flash photolysis, pump and probe, experiments,

described in 1949, gave only millisecond time resolution because of the very high energy, and consequently long duration, flash excitation sources which were used. Within a year or two, more sensitive detection allowed smaller flashes and resolution down to a few microseconds but little further improvement occurred for ten years, except in the measurement of fluorescence lifetimes where very small spark sources of a few nanoseconds duration gave adequate intensity for fluorescence measurement as more sensitive detectors and faster oscilloscopes became available.

The invention of the laser in 1960 was immediately recognised as the beginning of a new era but it was some time before sub-microsecond pulses were used in a flash photolysis experiment. Whilst the pump and probe in a microsecond flash experiment can be separate sources, synchronisation becomes increasingly difficult at shorter times and impossible in the picosecond regime. The principle of deriving the pump and probe pulses from the same source and separating them in time by an optical delay were used in an apparatus developed in this laboratory[1], following a demonstration that the Q-switched laser was indeed a powerful photochemical source for flash photolysis experiments[2] and a somewhat different application of the same principle was used by J.R. Novak and M.W. Windsor[3].

Although we were delighted to have extended the time resolution of flash photolysis by a factor of a thousand, the introduction of the mode-locked laser which occurred aobut this time soon extended the possibilities of short pulse times by a further factor of a thousand and, for most laboratories, nanoseconds became old-hat even before they had been used, and the transition was made directly from microseconds to picoseconds. At the present time the shortest pulses available from any source are those from the mode-locked lasers of Shank and his colleagues of Bell Laboratories, which are frequency broadened by self-phase modulation (in an optical fibre) and time shortened by a grating compressor to give a duration of about 30 femtoseconds[4]. The synchroton, whose applications are described by Dr Munro of the Daresbury Laboratory, is the principal alternative to mode-locked lasers in the picosecond field but at present its time resolution is less by a factor of about one thousand. This brings to an end not only my brief account of the development of short pulse generation for chemical and biological measurements but also the necessity for further development. The uncertainties in the wavelength and energy at these very short times are comparable with the wavelength and energy which is measured, as is shown by the examples in Table 1. At 1 femtosecond the uncertainty in energy is 400kJ/mole which is greater than the energy of most chemical bonds. It is often said that there are no 'instantaneous' reactions but this is not true if it means that no reactions are immeasurably fast in principle.

As far as detection techniques for these short pulse times are concerned, the real time streak-camera takes us down to one picosecond (as described by Dr Taylor) and pump-probe techniques can measure the shortest available pulses. We can therefore be content that any time resolution that we are ever likely to need in a chemical experiment is, or soon will be, available and devote more of our attention to making better use of these powerful new techniques. We have, in fact, already reached the stage where it is difficult to find chemical systems of real interest where the full time resolution of our new methods can be properly utilised. The principal molecular events which occur in the time region between one nanosecond and one picosecond are shown in figure 1 and it will be seen that few of them would be called chemistry by a chemist.

Table 1   Uncertainty in Sub-Picosecond Times

Δt (fs)	ΔE (kJ/mole)	ΔE (eV)	Δ (nm) (at λ = 500nm)
1000 (1 ps)	0.4	0.004	0.85
30	13	0.135	28
1	400	4.14	850

Chemical reactions usually proceed by a series of steps many of which, like the processes of activation, are extremely fast. The rate, as normally measured, is essentially determined by the rate of the slowest step in a sequence.

In a pulse experiment it is possible to follow separately some of the steps in the sequence but not all of them. In the kinetic study of a sequence of reactions it is *only possible to study those reactions which are slower than all preceding reactions in the sequence* (although by convolution methods some small overlap of rates may be resolvable). The first step in the sequence is excitation by the light flash and this determines the fastest rate which can be measured. The first chemical step determines the fastest second step which can be measured, and so on. This introduces a very serious limitation in the study of ordinary chemical reactions where the first step is the encounter of two species by a diffusion process which, even at high concentrations, is relatively slow on the time scale we are considering. As is seen in figure 1, even at molar concentrations, the average encounter time between solute molecules in a solution of viscosity 1 cp is of the order of 100 ps. In gases at 1 atm. pressure it is about the same.

What processes in chemistry or biology operate in the time region between 1 nanosecond and the few tens of

femtoseconds which is the limit of useful measurement
in chemical systems? They are still quite numerous
and they may be classified as follows:

Molecular physics

These are molecular processes which do not involve any
chemical change, *i.e* any change of chemical species
present. They are by far the most fruitful ground for
molecular picosecond studies and include most of the

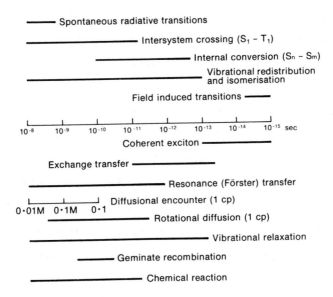

fundamental physical processes in solution, such as
vibrational and rotational relaxation where the encounter
time of solute with solvent molecules is less than one
picosecond. These should therefore be regarded as
bimolecular or multimolecular processes. The second
principal class of intermolecular physical processes
which are fast enough to fall in this range involve
energy transfer between molecules, which often occurs over
a range of nanometers and is therefore possible, without
mass diffusion, even at modest concentrations (above 10^{-3}M).

The other very fast physical processes are unimolecular
and involve intramolecular interaction, energy
redistribution and perhaps some small change of molecular
shape. The principal examples are *(a)* intramolecular
vibrational relaxation, which involves an isoenergetic
redistribution of vibrational quanta, and *(b)* redistribution of energy between electronic and vibrational levels.
The latter includes the very important photo-physical
processes of internal conversion and intersystem crossing
in which there is a transfer to a lower electronic level
accompanied by a transfer of an equivalent amount of
energy into vibrational modes. These processes may occur
in picosecond times even in an isolated molecule in the
gas phase.

Chemical change
As already discussed, intermolecular processes between

solute molecules are relatively slow at normal
concentrations. Physical interaction with the solvent is
fast but chemical change usually involves at least a small
activation energy and therefore longer times. One process
which may occur with negligible activation energy is
charge transfer to (or from) the solvent and, provided it
can occur without nuclear configurational change, it
becomes essentially a Franck-Condon transition within
the solute-solvent complex and may be immeasurably fast,
although one will usually observe subsequent relaxations
of the solvent shell about the solute ion[5]. Another
pseudo-intermolecular reaction[6] is the geminate cage
recombination of atoms which follows excitation of a
diatomic molecule in solution. Some of the fragments
never become really separated and recombination occurs
in a few picoseconds there are, in principle, many other
dissociation reactions in solution which are expected to
behave similarly.

The other large class of intramolecular chemical
reactions are isomerisations of the various kinds, many
of which occur in picosecond times. Although the
photochemical method allows us to prepare a non-
equilibrium concentration in the ground state and to
study relaxations in that state, much of the interest is
in the excited state relaxation, not only because it is
unavoidably involved in processes which are initiated
by photochemical methods but because configurational

changes in this state are often responsible for the
rapid internal conversion processes which occur. In
cyanine dyes, for example, it is the rotation, in
picosecond items, of one part of the molecule with respect
to another, that determines the Franck Condon factors, the
rates of radiationless conversion from one electronic
state to another and the fluorescence lifetime.
Indirectly, these phenomena, which are dependent on the
solvent viscosity, are, like rotational relaxation, a
means of studying microscopic details of solvent
interactions. These aspects will be illustrated in the
papers of Doust and of Sundstrom.

Picosecond biology

It will be clear, from what has already been said, that
picosecond processes must occur within the molecule, or
within an already formed molecular complex such as a
solvated molecule, unless the concentrations are very
high. Apart from solid state physics and chemistry, very
high concentrations are mainly a characteristic of
biological systems and it is for this reason that photo-
biology is one of the most important sciences where
picosecond time resolution is of prime importance. In
biological systems, physical and chemical interactions
occur between molecules which are already in close
proximity and the electron transfer processes already
referred to as well as proton transfers, become
commonplace between neighbouring 'solute' molecules.

The unimolecular processes of rotational diffusion,
studied by anisotropic fluorescence relaxation, are
also of particular importance in biology and allow us to
study such matters as the rotation of a prosthetic group
or part of a protein within the macroscopic entity.

In photosynthesis, the whole energy transfer process
between and within the various pigment beds, is complete
within a few hundred picoseconds even though they may
involve random-walk transfer between several hundred
pigment molecules. These are physical rather than
chemical processes, but the chemical processes of
electron transfer which occur in the reaction centre
also involve events whose first steps take place in a
few picoseconds.

Thus, although picosecond measurements are approaching
the limits of what is significant in chemistry and
biology, they are still an essential and fundamental
part of the story. Each decade of time, from a second
down to a picosecond has its own story to tell ... in
fact, over this range of time it may be argued that the
number of events of interest are more or less equal for
each decade of time. Each time range, and each technique
appropriate to its study, is therefore of interest but,
since it has become accessible so very recently,
picosecond chemistry and biology quite naturally command
our particular attention today.

References

1. G. Porter, Flash Photolysis and Primary Processes in
   the Excited State, *'Nobel Symposium 5 - Fast
   Reactions and Primary Processes in Chemical Kinetics'*
   Interscience Publishers, London, 1967, p.141.
   G. Porter and M.R. Topp, *Nature*, 1968, **220**,1228;
   Proc.Roy.Soc., 1970, *A315*, 163.

2. G. Porter and J.I. Steinfeld, *J. Chem.Phys.*, 1966,
   45, 3456.

3. J.R. Novak and M.W. Windsor, *J. Chem.Phys.*, 1967,**47**,
   3075; *Proc.Roy.Soc.*, 1968, **A308**, 95.

4. C.V. Shank, R.L. Fork, R.T. Yen, R.H. Stolen and W.J.
   Tomlinson, *Appl.Phys.Lett.*, 1982, 40, 761.

5. G.A. Kenney-Wallace, L.A. Hunt and K.L. Sala,
   Picosecond Phenomena 11, 1980,**203**.

6. T.J. Chuang, G.W. Hoffmann and K.B. Eisenthal, *Chem.
   Phys.Letters*, 1974, **25**,201.

Fluorescence Lifetime and Depolarisation Measurements using Frequency Up-conversion

T. Doust

Davy Faraday Research Laboratory, The Royal Institution, 21 Albemarle Street, London W1X 4BS

Abstract

The use of frequency mixing in a non linear crystal as a means of time resolving fluorescence is described. The technique is compared with other methods of time resolving fluorescence in the picosecond regime. Rotational diffusion rates of a dye in single and binary solvent systems have been measured and information obtained on solvation. Some new measurements of the short, viscosity dependent fluorescence lifetime of crystal violet in low viscosity solvents are presented.

Introduction

The non-linear optical phenomenon of frequency up-conversion can, when a suitably timed laser pulse is used as one component in the process, provide a useful means of gating fluorescence signals with picosecond time resolution. The technique has been used by a number of workers to study a variety of chemical and biological systems[1-15]. The purpose of this paper is to present a simple description of the theory of the up-conversion process, to discuss the practicalities of using the technique, to describe its application in this laboratory to two chemical problems and to briefly review other applications of the technique. Up-conversion is not a particularly easy technique to use so some consideration is given as to where it is appropriate and to where other techniques for measuring emission decay kinetics such as streak cameras or single photon counting methods may be more useful. Both these techniques are discussed in more detail in other papers in this book.

Theory

The theory of non-linear optics is covered in great detail in a number of textbooks (e.g. *Reference 16*); the object here is to present a minimal treatment containing sufficient information to characterise the up-conversion process. In the general case of optical frequency conversion in a non-linear crystal where ω_1 and ω_2 are the frequencies of the two input optical fields and ω_3 is the frequency of the output optical field, equation 1 is obeyed

$$\omega_3 = \omega_1 \pm \omega_2 \qquad \dots \ (1)$$

In the more familiar case of frequency doubling or second harmonic generation (SHG) $\omega_1 = \omega_2$, hence, $\omega_3 = 2\omega_1$; ω_1 and ω_2 are both derived from the same optical field. For optimal conversion efficiency equation 2 must be satisfied

$$\Delta\vec{k} = \vec{k}_3 - (\vec{k}_1 + \vec{k}_2) = 0$$

$$\dots \ (2)$$

or $\qquad \vec{k}_3 = \vec{k}_1 + \vec{k}_2$

where $\vec{k}$ is defined by equation 3

$$\vec{k}_i = \frac{n_i\,\omega_i\,\vec{r}_i}{c} \;; \qquad i = 1,2,3 \qquad \cdots (3)$$

Equation (2) is known as the phase matching condition and equation (3) defines the wave vectors of the input and output optical fields; n is the refractive index of the crystal, ω is the optical frequency, c is the velocity of light in vacuo and $\vec{r}$ is the unit vector orthogonal to the wave front. In the case of SHG, as mentioned above, $\omega_1 = \omega_2$, $n_1 = n_2$ and usually $\vec{r}_1 = \vec{r}_2$, (i.e. a single laser beam is passed through the crystal) then $\vec{k}_3 = 2\vec{k}_1$. The phase matching requirement arises because the ω_3 field generated at each point along the propagation direction in the crystal must be in phase with the ω_3 field generated at every other point otherwise destructive interference will occur. For up-conversion where there are two separate input beams at different frequencies it is necessary to consider the fact that $n_1(\omega_1) \neq n_2(\omega_2)$ and that the $\vec{r}_{1,2}$ may not be colinear.

Phase matching may be achieved by means of the birefringence of nonlinear crystals; the crystal will support the propagation of two optical fields with orthogonal polarisations with different refractive indices n_o and n_e, the ordinary and extraordinary refractive indices respectively. $n_e(\omega)$ depends on both the direction of propagation and the temperature so, by manipulating the polarisation of one or both of the input beams and the incidence angle on the crystal or the crystal temperature it is possible to obtain

phase matching. The frequencies that can be phase matched
depend on the crystal and the range of variation of n_e
with angle or the physical limitations to the crystal
temperature.

For a parallel input beam the conversion efficiency
will often depend critically on the crystal angle or the
temperature. However, if the incident beams of light are
focussed then the incident cone of light will contain a
range of angles and if the slope of the angle tuning curve,
$d\theta/d\omega$, is small then the range of angles in the incident
cone may allow phase matching over a wide range of
frequencies. Conversely, an appropriate choice of crystal
angle and focussing optics may allow the conversion of a
narrow band of fluorescence and give fairly good spectral
resolution. Figure 1 shows the tuning curve for lithium
iodate; data for many other non-linear materials is
available in the literature and from manufacturers.

To gate fluorescence by up-conversion it is necessary
to focus the fluorescence and the appropriately delayed
gating pulse through the same region of the crystal. The
gating pulse is derived from the pulse used to excite the
fluorescence and is delayed by varying the optical path
length; this is discussed in more detail later. The
power of the light generated at the sum frequency is given
by equation (4).

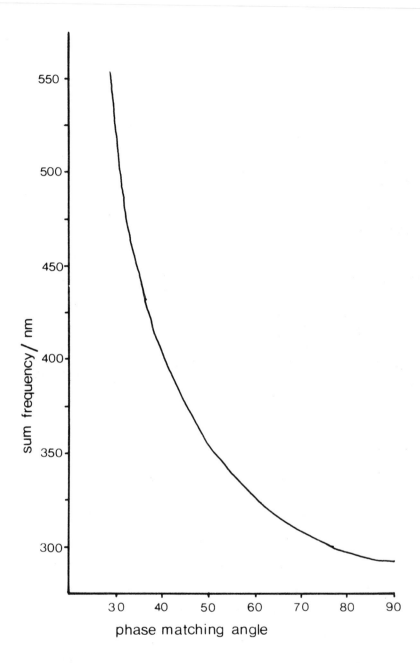

Figure 1   Angle tuning curve for lithium iodate

$$P_3 = P_2 \, P_1 \, dl^2 \, \frac{\omega_3}{\omega_2} \qquad \ldots \ (4)$$

where P is the power, the subscripts 1,2 and 3 refer to the
gating pulse, the fluorescence and the output respectively, l
is the length of the crystal and d is a collection of the
constants of a particular crystal. Remembering that P_1 is
constant from pulse to pulse and that the time duration of the
gating pulse is short compared with the fluorescence then
clearly P_3 at a particular time delay is proportional to the
average intensity of the fluorescence over the duration of the
gating pulse. P_3 can be averaged over many pulses at a
particular delay and varying the delay will allow the
fluorescence decay profile to be mapped out. This is
illustrated in figure 2. The exact temporal profile of P_3
cannot be readily evaluated analytically but it is of no
relevance as the lock-in detection system observes a d.c.
signal at any particular time delay as the individual pulses
are not resolved.

The angular or temperature dependence of the phase matching
allows tuning of the crystal to a particular spectral band of
the fluorescence. As was pointed out earlier the bandwidth
will depend on the crystal and the optics used. Henceforth,
the discussion will be restricted to angle tuning but most of
what is said is equally applicable to temperature tuning. A
convenient approach is to consider that at a particular
crystal angle the system is phase matched for a particular
value of ω_3. Equation (1) must be satisfied so a particular

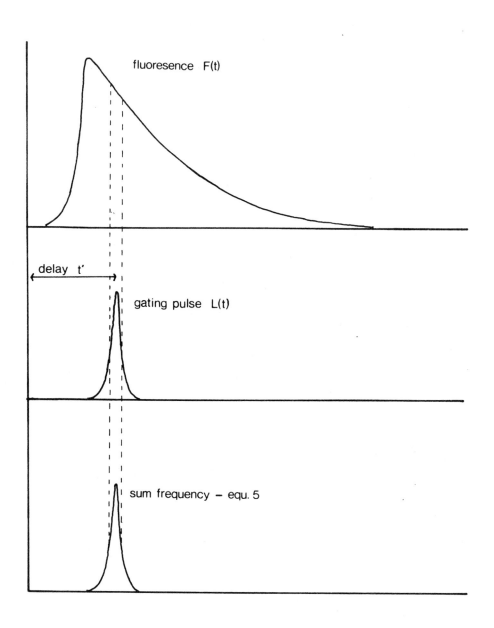

Figure 2   Fluorescence gating by up-conversion

value of ω_1, the laser frequency, will result in the
conversion of fluorescence at (or around) some frequency
ω_2. To tune across the fluorescence band there are two
possibilities: (a) fix ω_3 and vary ω_1 and (b) fix ω_1 and vary
ω_3 by altering the crystal angle. If the laser is tunable
(e.g. a synchronously pumped dye laser) method (a) is
far easier but has the disadvantage that as the gating
pulse (ω_1) is the same as that used to excite the
fluorescence then the excitation wavelength is being
varied. Method (b) is more difficult as it involves
moving the crystal but has the advantage that the
excitation wavelength is kept constant. If the laser is
not tunable then (b) is the only possible method. The
limitations to the tunability of a particular crystal are
due to reflection losses at the input and output faces
and to restrictions imposed by the aperture of the crystal
mount.

Three major factors limit the time resolution of an
up-conversion measurement; the precision with which the
optical delay can be positioned, group velocity dispersion
in the crystal and the width of the laser pulse. The
first of these is rarely a problem because stepper motor
driven translators are commercially available that can
be positioned to within 10 microns (an optical delay of
30 fs) or better. Piezo-electric devices can be
positioned even more precisely. Group velocity dispersion
is a potential problem and is dependent on the crystal

and the optics used; this is discussed in *Reference 10*. The laser pulse width is probably the most serious limitation but can be allowed for in the data analysis by the use of deconvolution techniques[17].

The signal at the optical frequency ω_3 observed at the detector, as a function of the optical delay t' is given by equation (5).

$$S(t') = \int_{-\infty}^{\infty} F(t) L(t-t') \, dt \qquad \dots (5)$$

where F(t) is the fluorescence from the sample and L(t) is the gating function (which happens to be the laser pulse shape). F(t) is the convolution of the molecular fluorescence decay function I(t) with the excitation pulse shape which is also L(t), equation (6).

$$F(t) = \int_{0}^{t} L(t') I(t-t') dt' \qquad \dots (6)$$

Inserting equation (6) into equation (5) and noting that equation (7)

$$g(t') = \int_{-\infty}^{\infty} L(t') L(t-t') \, dt \qquad \dots (7)$$

is the autocorrelation function of the laser pulse allows S(t') to be written as equation (8),

$$S(t') = \int_{0}^{t} G(t') I(t-t') \, dt' \qquad \dots (8)$$

which is the convolution of the molecular fluorescence decay function with the autocorrelation function of the laser pulse. This autocorrelation function can readily be measured and is additionally useful as a diagnostic for the laser mode-locking. The application of deconvolution procedures to the data analysis will allow the recovery of decay times at least

as short as the width of the autocorrelation function.
Figure 3 illustrates clearly the distortion due to the
convolution with the autocorrelation function, in this
case the laser pulse was badly mode-locked; the 'wings'
characteristic of the dye laser cavity being too short
are clearly visible, positioned symmetrically about the
rising edge of the fluorescence signal.

Practicalities

Figure 4 shows the optical arrangement used for the
experiments described later. The laser system is a
mode-locked Coherent CR12 argon ion laser synchronously
pumping a model 590 dye laser with an extended cavity.
The output consists of a continuous train of pulses of
typically 5 ps duration at a repetition rate of 75 MHz.
The output wavelength and tuning range depend, of course,
on the dye used; in this work rhodamine 6G was used around
590nm.

The beamsplitter B_1 directs half of each pulse into the
variable delay and the remainder is used to excite the
sample. The variable delay consists of a corner-cube
prism mounted on a stepper motor driven translation
stage. The undelayed portion of each pulse is focussed
into the sample with an 80mm focal length lens. The
sample is either flowed through a 1mm path length glass
cell or, preferably, pumped through a jet. If the sample
is static the solvent in the excited region is heated
resulting in thermal lensing and other undesirable effects.

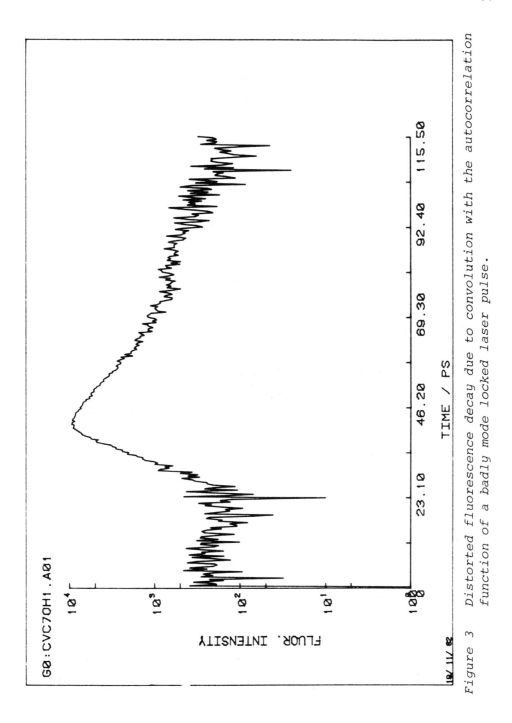

Figure 3   Distorted fluorescence decay due to convolution with the autocorrelation
function of a badly mode locked laser pulse.

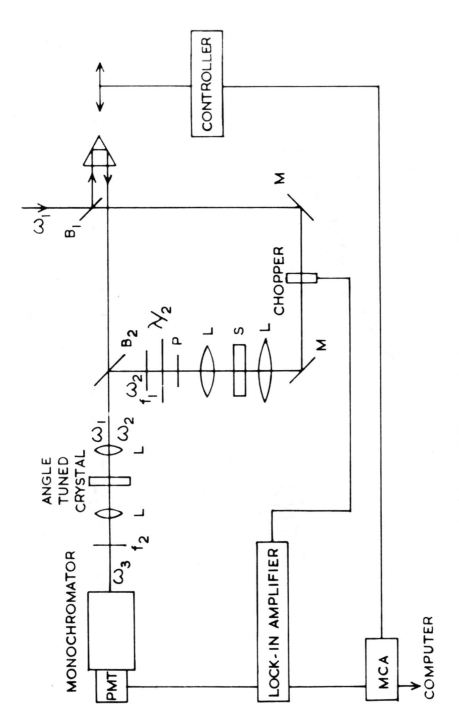

Figure 4   Schematic of the optical arrangement for up-conversion

The excitation polarisation can be varied if required with a half wave retarder.

The fluorescence is collected with a 100mm focal length achromatic lens and passed through a polariser oriented to transmit vertically polarised light and a high pass coloured glass filter that blocks the original excitation light. It is then combined with the delayed pulse at the beamsplitter B_2 and focussed into a 2mm thick $LiIO_3$ crystal cut at 55 degrees to the optic axis. The phase matching scheme used with this crystal requires both input beams to be polarised parallel; hence, to measure fluorescence polarised perpendicularly to the excitation light or at the magic angle it is necessary to vary the excitation polarisation.

The output of the crystal is focussed onto the slits of a monochromator. At this point there is laser light at the fundamental frequency, the fluorescence, second harmonic laser light and the up-converted light (in decreasing order of intensity). Although the monochromator goes a long way towards extracting the signal of interest the use of a lock-in amplifier with modulation provided by a chopper in the excitation beam is necessary and allows the up-converted signal to be amplified very selectively.

The output of the lock-in amplifier is fed into a voltage to frequency converter which produces a train of pulses at a rate proportional to the output voltage of the lock-in.

These pulses are counted into one particular channel of a multichannel analyser which is indexed by the position of the optical delay. After a complete scan of the optical delay the contents of the analyser represent the signal intensity as a function of the delay. The data can then be transferred to a computer for storage and analysis.

The different operational characteristics of different approaches to this technique arise largely from the use of different types of laser. The instrument of Mahr et al[1-3] also used a synchronously pumped dye laser and apart from the fact that the optical arrangement prevented analysis of the fluorescence polarisation behaved in a similar fashion to the instrument described here.

Topp has used a mode locked Nd:YAG laser with a regenerative amplifier to produce pulses 12ps long at a wavelength of 1.06 microns. The second or third harmonic of this is used for excitation and the fundamental infrared light is used for gating. The advantages of this approach are that the high peak power of the pulses make the frequency conversion more efficient so that less extreme focussing (and the associated alignment problems) is required and that the 1.06 micron gating wavelength imparts less of a blue shift to the detected signal than gating with, say, a 600 nm pulse; this allows shorter wavelength fluorescence to be up-converted without running into

problems from the crystal transmission cutting off in the u.v.
A potential disadvantage is that the low repetition rate
requires sample and hold or boxcar type signal averaging
systems which often require longer periods of signal averaging
than the high repetition rate lock-in based detection systems
to achieve the same signal to noise improvement. A further
point to consider is that the pulse shapes of the fundamental
and the second harmonic are not the same and the observed
signal is the convolution of the fluorescence with the cross
correlation function of these two pulses although in principle
this function is no more difficult to measure than the
autocorrelation function. By a judicious choice of crystal
and focussing optics Topp et al[11] have managed to up-convert
a large bandwidth of fluorescence allowing complete time
resolved emission spectra to be recorded; down-conversion,
i.e. $\omega_3 = \omega_2 - \omega_1$ has also been demonstrated with this
instrument.

The instrument used by Gochanour and Fayer[9] falls somewhere between the two approaches already discussed. They
use a c.w. mode-locked Nd:YAG laser producing 140 ps pulses
at 1.06 microns. The high repetition rate allows the use of
lock-in detection and the advantages of using infrared gating
pulses are the same as with Topp's instrument. The major
disadvantage is that the rather long pulse from this type of
laser limits time resolution somewhat.

Comparison with other methods of time resolving luminescence
is not particularly easy; the two most commonly used techniques

are streak cameras and time correlated single photon counting. If the cost of the laser is ignored then the streak camera is the most expensive, but it is far easier to use as there is no need for moving optics, complicated alignment etc. As far as time resolution is concerned single photon counting is limited to around 20 ps at the absolute best, streak cameras currently to around 1-2 ps whereas up-conversion is limited mainly by the width of the laser pulse which may be as short as 100 fs or less. In spectral sensitivity streak cameras and single photon counting work well in the visible and near u.v. but the sensitivity drops off rapidly in the red and near i.r. unless special photocathodes are used on the image converter or photomultiplier tubes. Up-conversion is inconvenient to use in the blue and u.v. because the signal is shifted into spectral regions where the transmission is low in conventional crystalline non-linear materials. However, in the red and near infrared it is very sensitive; the $LiIO_3$ crystal used in this work can be tuned for fluorescence from 630 nm to greater than 1 micron when the gating pulses are at 600 nm. The linearity and dynamic range of single photon counting and up-conversion are usually much greater than can be obtained with a single shot streak camera and often better than can be obtained with synchroscan type cameras.

Clearly, the choice of technique depends on the

nature of the luminescence. If the decay time is longer than
100 ps or so and it is in the visible or u.v. then single
photon counting is the cheapest and easiest technique to use.
Similarly if it is faster than this but in the same spectral
region and the kinetics are relatively simple then the streak
camera, although expensive, is easier to use (and probably
more productive!) However, for fast and possibly complex
decay kinetics in the red or near infrared then up-conversion
is probably the most satisfactory technique to use. In an
ideal world it would be useful to have all three techniques
and perhaps others available in one's laboratory.

Applications

Up-conversion has been applied to two problems in this
laboratory; *(a)* the measurement of rotational diffusion rates
from time resolved fluorescence depolarisation and *(b)* the
measurement of viscosity dependent non-radiative relaxation
rates in triphenylmethane dyes. Both these problems have
been discussed at some length in the literature[4-8] so the
intention here is just to briefly review this work (with more
emphasis on the rotational diffusion work) and to briefly
review the applications to which the instruments in other
laboratories described in the previous section have been put.

a) Fluorescence depolarisation

If an assembly of molecules, randomly orientated (e.g. in
fluid solution), is excited with plane polarised light, a
particular orientational population distribution will be

obtained in the excited state due to the dependence of the
absorption probability on the angle between the transition
moment and the electric field of the light. Brownian
motion will randomise the excited state orientations
ultimately resulting in a homogeneous population
distribution. As the fluorescence polarisation (with
respect to some external coordinate system) depends on the
orientation of the transition moment the fluorescence will,
with time, become depolarised due to the decay of the
inhomogeneity of the excited state orientational population
distribution; this assumes that the excited state is
sufficiently long lived for the randomisation to occur.
Thus the rate of fluorescence depolarisation is related to
the orientational correlation function of the excited state
molecule. This orientational relaxation can be a very
sensitive probe of the microenvironment of a fluorescent
species due to its dependence on the size and shape of the
rotor, its interaction with its environment and the
microviscosity and microstructure of the environment. This
is not confined to whole molecules, the restricted motion
of a fluorophore in a macromolecule (e.g tryptophan in a
protein) can also induce fluorescence anisotropy.

Equation (9) defines the time dependent anisotropy, $r(t)$

$$r(t) = \frac{I_{//}(t) - I_{\perp}(t)}{I_{//}(t) + 2I_{\perp}(t)} \qquad \ldots (9)$$

where $I_{//}(t)$ and $I_{\perp}(t)$ are the intensities of fluorescence polarised parallel and perpendicularly respectively to the excitation polarisation. Figure 5 is a plot of the measured $I_{//}(t)$ and $I_{\perp}(t)$ components of the fluorescence of cresyl violet in ethanol; two exponential components are clearly visible in each decay curve. The fast component of $I_{//}(t)$ is due to the initial decrease in the population oriented parallel to the direction of the excitation polarisation and the initial grow-in of the $I_{\perp}(t)$ component is due to the increasing population oriented perpendicularly to the excitation polarisation. The longer component in both curves is the decay of the total excited state population; note that at longer times, when the population distribution has become homogeneous $I_{//} = I_{\perp}$. Figure 6 shows the anisotropy $r(t)$ calculated from the curves in figure 5 using equation (9).

One of the problems associated with analysing time resolved anisotropy on the picosecond and nanosecond time scales is the deconvolution of the instrument response function; the response is usually assumed to be the same for both polarisation components. This problem is rendered unimportant if up-conversion is used because on the time scale of the data in figures 5 and 6 the instrument response is less than 9 ps wide and can safely be ignored. In the case of free rotational diffusion the anisotropy should eventually decay to zero and as mentioned above $I_{//}(t) = I_{\perp}(t)$ at long times. This can be used to detect the independence of the

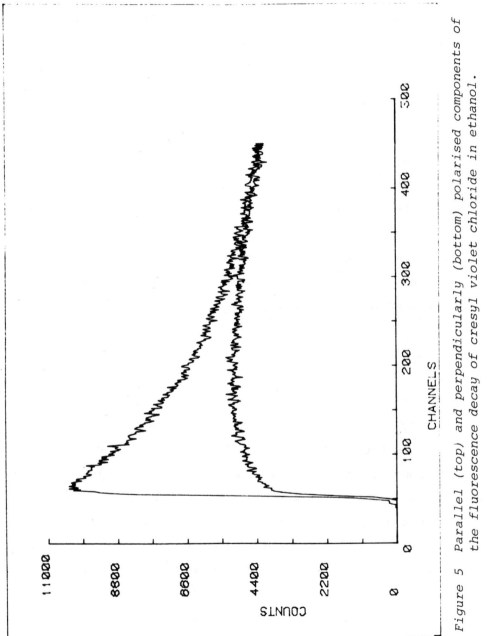

Figure 5 Parallel (top) and perpendicularly (bottom) polarised components of the fluorescence decay of cresyl violet chloride in ethanol.

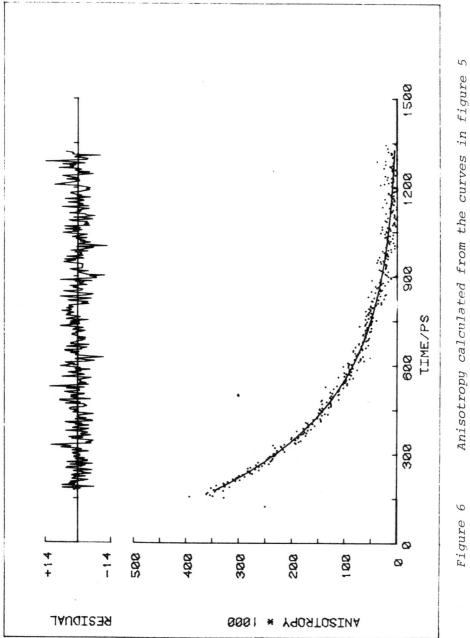

Figure 6   Anisotropy calculated from the curves in figure 5

detection sensitivity to the polarisation of the
fluorescence. If the available optical delay is not long
enough to allow the anisotropy to decay to zero it is
useful to set up the instrument using a sample in which
the anisotropy is known to decay rapidly.

In the Debye-Stokes-Einstein model of rotational
diffusion, which describes the simple case of sphere
rotating in a hydrodynamic continuum, the anisotropy
decay is related to solvent and solute properties by
equations (10) and (11)

$$r(t) = r_0 \exp(-t/\tau_R) \qquad \ldots (10)$$

$$R = \frac{V\eta}{kT} \qquad \ldots (11)$$

where V is the volume of the rotor and η is the solvent
viscosity. This model can be extended for arbitrary
shapes by the inclusion of the so-called 'stick' factor,
f, as in equation (12)

$$R = \frac{V\eta f}{kT} \qquad \ldots (12)$$

f = 1 for a sphere; f > 1 for any other shape.

The stick interaction involves frictional drag on the
rotor and displacement of solvent if the rotor is not
spherical; 'slip' behaviour is not considered here.

Although the approximations are gross, the linear

behaviour of τ_R with η is observed surprisingly often although the slope often deviates from Vf/kT and the intercept is rarely zero. These deviations, bearing in mind that V and f can be calculated, can, with careful interpretation, provide information about solvent-solute interaction that is greater or less than that on which the model is based. Figure 7 is a plot of τ_R against viscosity for the dyes cresyl violet and oxazine-1 in a series of solvents of varying viscosity along with the lines calculated from equation (12). Clearly, oxazine-1 follows the predicted behaviour quite closely, whereas cresyl violet deviates strongly from the predicted line except when the solvent is water.

This behaviour has been explained as follows[5]. Figure 8 shows the structure of the two dyes; the only functional difference is that the two amino groups are ethylated in oxazine-1. In cresyl violet there is a strong hydrogen bonding interaction (with the amino groups acting as donors) with all the solvents except water. As a result the dye has to drag solvent molecules with it as it moves and the diffusion rate is reduced and τ_R is increased. Alternatively it could be said that the effective volume of the rotor is increased. With oxazine-1 this interaction site is blocked by the ethylation and the rotor is simply the unsolvated dye. The same is true for cresyl violet in water. Although water is normally regarded as a strong hydrogen bonding solvent it seems that in the case of these dyes that the water-water interaction is greater than the water-dye interaction.

24

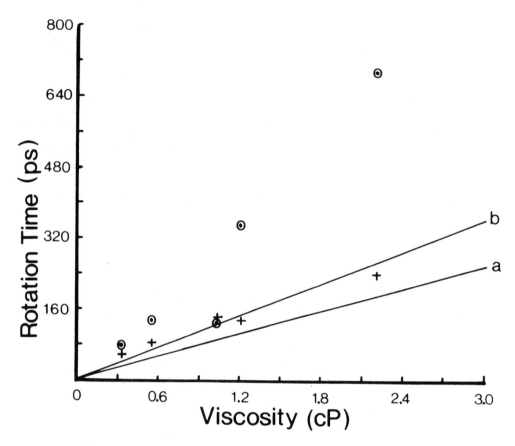

Figure 7

Plot of the rotational relaxation time against viscosity
for cresyl violet and oxazine-1 in a variety of solvents
along with the lines calculated from equation (12), (a) for
cresyl violet, (b) for oxazine-1

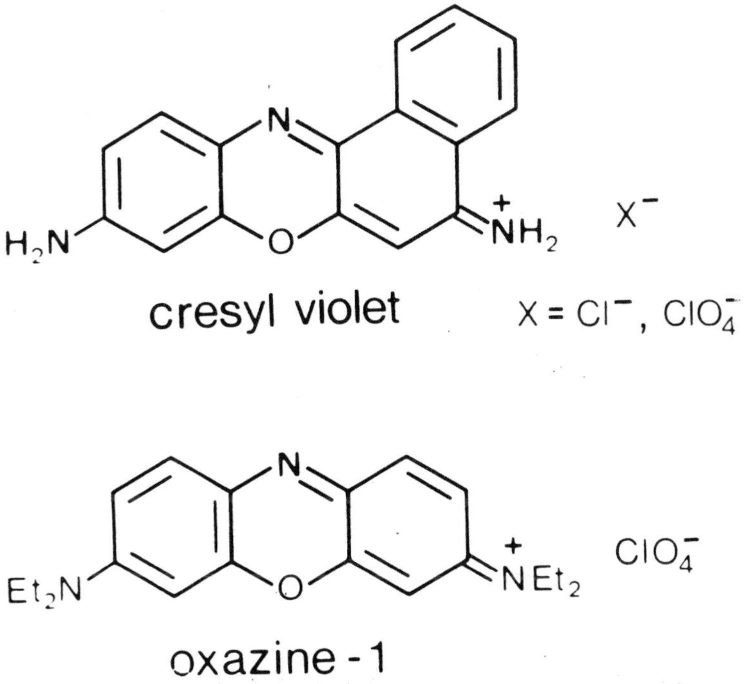

Figure 8   *The structures of cresyl violet and oxazine-1*

This study has been extended to investigate the behaviour in mixed solvents; this is discussed in more detail elsewhere[6]. Briefly, in many mixtures of organic solvents with water (e.g. alcohols, DMSO) the viscosity goes through a maximum as the fraction of the organic component is increased. The rotational relaxation time of cresyl violet increases linearly with viscosity up to the maximum viscosity with the slope calculated for the unsolvated dye molecule after which it varies non-linearly

towards the value for the pure organic component; a
typical curve is shown in figure 9. The implication is
that in the linear region the organic component is
involved in the waters hydrogen bonding networks rather
than solvating the dye. This extends up to the maximum
viscosity. In the non-linear region above the maximum
viscosity the structure of the solvent is broken up due to
the excess of organic component which is then available
to solvate the dye.

b) Fluorescence of triphenylmethane dyes
This class of dyes has been known for a long time to have
low, viscosity dependent fluorescence quantum yields and
lifetimes. This behaviour, which is also found in
cyanine and some other dyes is thought to be due to
excited state conformational relaxation leading to
enhanced non-radiative decay rates[18]. Models of this
behaviour have predicted to a greater or lesser extent the
observed excited state decay kinetics[18-20] but in low

viscosity solvents, where the fluorescence quantum yield is
low and the excited state lifetime short (2-20 ps), there
has been very little experimental data available, particularly
fluorescence lifetime data. Up-conversion is an ideal
technique for studying this system as it is sensitive in the
red, has sufficient linearity and dynamic range to cope with
multi-exponential kinetics and the time resolution (with
deconvolution) to measure the shortest decays.

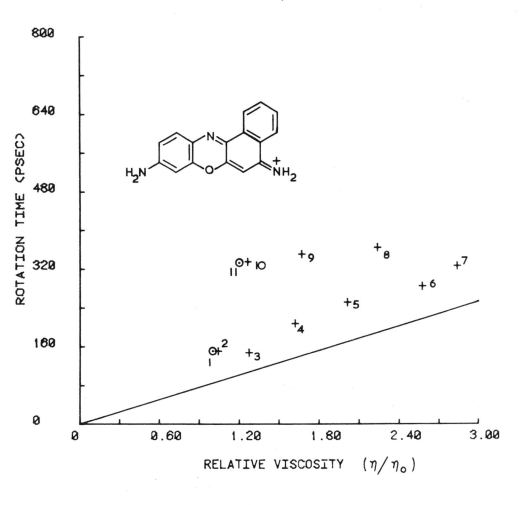

Figure 9

Plot of the rotational relaxation time of cresyl violet
against viscosity for a series of ethanol-water mixtures.
Points 1 and 11 are pure water and pure ethanol respectively.

The fluorescence decay of crystal violet, whose structure is shown in figure 10, was measured in a series of monohydric alcohols, hexan-1-ol through undecan-1-ol and the diols ethan-1 2-diol and propan-1,3-diol. Dual exponential kinetics were observed in all cases; the results are plotted logarithmically in figure 11. For the monohydric alcohols the empirical relationship

$$\tau_f = c \ \eta^{\alpha} \qquad \dots \ (13)$$

where η is the viscosity, is obeyed in a similar fashion to earlier studies of this system and to cyanine dyes. In this case $\alpha = 0.82$ for the slower component and $\alpha = 0.30$ for the fast component.

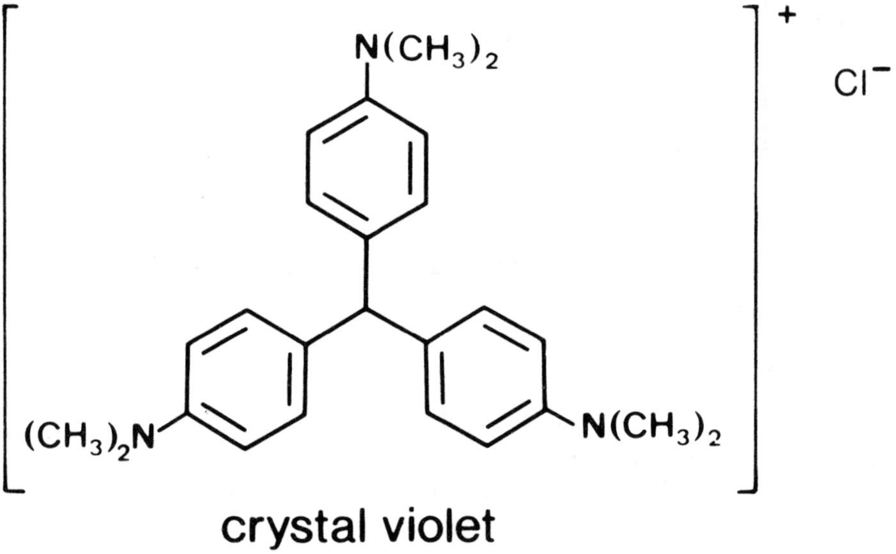

crystal violet

Figure 10   The structure of crystal violet

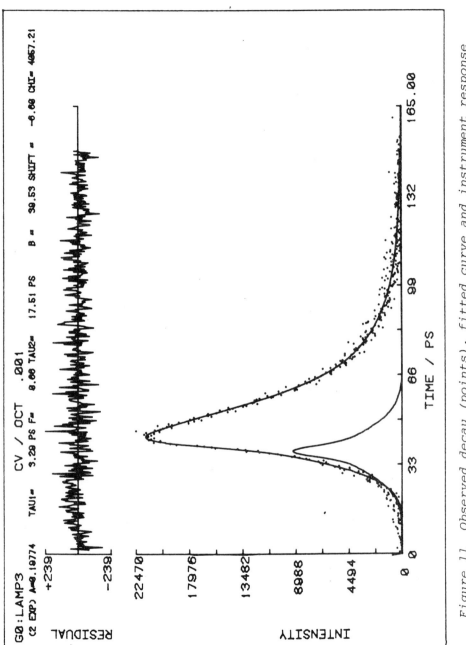

*Figure 11 Observed decay (points), fitted curve and instrument response
function (solid lines) for crystal violet in 1-octanol.*

These measurements are complementary to and apparently
consistent with the ground state recovery measurements of
Sundstrom *et al* discussed elsewhere in this book. The
detailed interpretation of these results is beyond the scope
of this paper but they are discussed futher elsewhere[21].
However, attention is drawn to the anomously low lifetimes in
the diols. Whilst with only two data points any fit to
equation (13) is meaningless, this behaviour has been
observed in cyanine dyes[22] and in the rotational
diffusion of whole molecules[23]. It appears that this
behaviour may be fairly general and there is evidence that
this is due to differences in the solvent-solvent
interaction rather than the solvent-dye interaction.

c) Other applications

It was mentioned earlier that up-conversion has been used
in one form or another by other workers. This section
covers briefly some of the chemical and biological
applications. The first application to the measurement of
time resolved luminescence (as opposed to laser frequency
conversion or pulse diagnostics) was by Mahr and Hirsch[1]
who up-converted the fluorescence of rhodamine 6G with
mode-locked argon ion laser pulses at 514.5nm in an angle
tuned ammonium dihydrogen phosphate (ADP) crystal; this
demonstrated the feasibility of the technique.
Subsequently, using a synchronously pumped dye laser,
Mahr *et al*[2] measured the emission lifetime of bacteriorhodopsin. The low power, high repetition rate tunable

pulses allowed very selective excitation of particular chromophores. Fluorescence was detected in the region 779-782 nm and a lifetime of 15 ± 3 ps was recorded. The same instrument was used in a study of the fluorescence of malachite green[3] (another triphenylmethane dye) in a similar way to and for the same reasons as the study of crystal violet reported here. More viscous solvent systems were used and dual component fluorescence lifetimes down to about 5 ps for the fast component were measured.

Gochanour and Fayer have used their instrument to measure fluorescence depolarisation rates in a study of energy transfer amongst randomly orientated rhodamine 6G molecules in solution[9]. With the use of appropriate deconvolution techniques the 100 ps pulses from their continuously mode locked Nd:YAG laser provided adequate time resolution for this study. The single shot system built by Topp *et al* was originally used to measure the fluorescence from rhodamine 6G and erythrosin and the S_2 fluorescence from xanthione[10]; the performance of this system is typified by the conversion of 470 nm fluorescence from xanthione to 325 nm with a measured lifetime of 14 ± 2ps. Later developments of this instrument allowed the conversion of large bandwidths of fluorescence to produce time resolved emission spectra of 3,4,9,10-dibenzpyrene in hexane at 300K over about 30 ps[11]. The same techniques were later used to time resolve emission spectra from vibrationally excited B_u states of diphenyl polyenes[12].

Conclusions

It has been demonstrated that up-conversion can be a useful technique for time resolving luminescence on a picosecond time scale. The overall characteristics of the technique are dependent to a large extent on the type of laser used for excitation and gating. For emission in the red and near i.r. that decays rapidly or with complex kinetics the time resolution, dynamic range and sensitivity are superior to other techniques.

Acknowledgements

The financial support of the SERC is gratefully acknowledged as is the encouragement and advice of Professor Sir George Porter. In particular, acknowledgement is due to Dr G.S. Beddard who was very much involved in the development of the instrument described herein and in the rotational diffusion work.

References

1. H. Mahr and M. Hirsch, *Opt. Commun.*, 13,96, (1975).

2. M. Hirsch, M. Marcus, A. Lewis, H. Mahr and N. Frigo, *Biophys. J.*, 16,1399, (1976).

3. M. Hirsch and H. Mahr, *Chem. Phys. Letts.*, 60, 299, (1979).

4. G. Beddard, T. Doust and M. Windsor, *Picosecond Phenomena II (eds. R. Hochstrasser, W. Kaiser and C. Shank) (Springer-Verlag, Berlin, 1980), p.167.

5. G. Beddard, T. Doust and G. Porter, *Chem. Phys.*, 61, 17, (1981).

6. G. Beddard, T. Doust and J. Hudales, *Nature,* 294,145, (1981).

7. G. Beddard, T. Doust, S. Meech and D. Phillips, *J.Photochem.*, 17, 427, (1981).

8. T. Doust and G. Beddard*, Picosecond Phenomena III, (eds. K. Eisenthal, R. Hochstrasser, W. Kaiser and A. Laubereau) (Springer-Verlag, Berlin, 1982), p.232.

9. C.Gochanour and M. Fayer, *J. Phys. Chem.*, 85, 1989, (1981).

10. L. Halliday and M. Topp, *Chem. Phys. Letts.*, 46, 8, (1977).

11. K. J. Choi, B. Boczar and M. Topp, *Chem. Phys.*, 57, 415, (1981).

12. T. Felder, K.J. Choi, and M. Topp, *Chem. Phys.*, 64, 175, (1982).

13. K.J. Choi, L. Halliday and M. Topp as reference 4, p.131.

14.   B. Boczar and M. Topp, as reference 8, p.174.

15.   B. Bushak, A. Rubinov, A. Murav'ov and A. Stupak, as reference 8, p.246.

16.   A. Yariv, *Quantum Electronics*, 2nd edn., (Wiley, New York, 1975).

17.   D. O'Connor, W.Ware and J. Andre, *J. Phys. Chem.*, **83**, 1333, (1979).

18.   Th. Forster and G. Hoffman, *Z. Physik. Chem.*, NF75, 63, (1971).

19.   D. Cremers and M. Windsor, *Chem. Phys. Letts.*, **71**, 27, (1980).

20.   V. Sundstrom, T. Gillbro and H. Bergstrom, *Chem. Phys.*, **73**, 439, (1982).

21.   T. Doust, *Chem. Phys. Letts.*, **96**, 522, (1983).

22.   A. Winkworth, A. Osborne and G. Porter, as reference 8, p.228.

23.   R. Moog, M. Ediger, S.Boxer and M. Fayer, *J. Phys. Chem.*, **86**,4694, (1982).

Picosecond Laser Spectroscopy and Magnetic Resonance Studies on Isolated Chlorophyll-proteins

G.F.W. Searle, A. van Hoek and T.J. Schaafsma

Department of Molecular Physics, Agricultural University, de Dreijen 11, 6703 BC Wageningen, The Netherlands

Abstract

Isolated, purified chlorophyll-proteins represent the building blocks from which the in vivo photosynthetic apparatus is constructed. We have investigated two major chlorophyll-proteins from barley, using both 293K fluorescence decay kinetics and chlorophyll triplet state properties at 4.2K.

The photosystem I reaction-centre protein, Chl_a-P1, shows a major 40 ps component in the fluorescence decay kinetics in the long wavelength emission of the antenna Chl *a*, which is interpreted as the time for energy migration to photo-chemically active reaction centres. Charge separation results in the formation of triplets, which can be observed by Fluorescence-Detected Magnetic Resonance (FDMR). The sign-inversion of the 4.2K FDMR spectrum w.r.t. that predicted from Fluorescence Fading (FF) experiments can be explained by singlet energy transfer from the antenna to the reaction center. Oxidation of the primary donor results in the loss of its triplet FDMR signal. The 293K fluorescence life-time is close to the time resolution of the measuring system (mode-locked

Ar[+] laser/single photon counting detection requiring deconvolution analysis), so that care has been taken to check the instrument performance. A Philips PM 2254B photomultiplier was used, which did not show detectable wavelength-dependence of photoelectron transit times. The light harvesting protein containing both Chl a and b, Chl_{ab}-P2, whose function is to channel singlet excitation energy rapidly and efficiently to the reaction centre proteins, shows two components (2.5 and 4.7 ns) in the 293K fluorescence decay kinetics of Chl a. This suggests an unexpected complexity in the energy transfer mechanism. We present a model for this protein containing two types of Chl a, that which is closely associated with Chl b and that which is relatively 'isolated'.

Introduction

The development of the mode-locked Ar[+] laser/single photon counting detection system for measurements of fluorescence decay kinetics of biological samples at low excitation intensity can for a great part be credited to Beddard and Fleming working in Sir George Porter's laboratory at the Royal Institution[1]. It is therefore appropriate that our contribution to this proceedings should be concerned with measurements made in Wageningen on a similar set-up constructed in cooperation with Dr Bebelaar, University of Amsterdam. Coupled to fluorescence decay kinetics, we have also studied chlorophyll triplet state properties at liquid helium temperature, because it has been shown that Fluorescence Detected Magnetic Resonance (FDMR) spectra can give valuable information on the microenvironment of chlorophyll, in particular ligation to Mg and ring V (see reference 2 for a comprehensive review). We recently presented a preliminary characterization of the chlorophyll-proteins isolated from barley (wild-type and mutant strains), which are also the objects for study in the present report[3].

Considerable emphasis is placed on a description of the picosecond laser set-up in order to give a picture of the present state of development of this type of system. Also the equipment needed for triplet state studies is detailed as these techniques may be less well known: using the same set-up we can measure FDMR spectra and kinetics, and Fluorescence Fading (FF) curves, which give triplet spin level population rates and decay rate constants[4].

Experimental

i)   Chlorophyll-proteins

Photosystem I chlorophyll-protein (Chl_a - P1) and light harvesting chlorophyll a/b-protein (Chl_{ab} - P2) have been isolated from barley as has been described previously[3,5].

The samples were small (about 2x2x2mm cube) pieces of polyacrylamide electrophoresis gel containing the chlorophyll-protein. These were stored at 77K until use.

The picosecond fluorescence kinetics experiments were carried out at room temperature (20°C), and because of the proteins' instability for long periods at this temperature, the measurements were completed within 5-10 min and a fresh piece of gel sample was taken for each measurement. FDMR and fluorescence fading experiments were all performed at 4.2K.

ii)   *Picosecond spectroscopy*

   In figure 1 a block diagram of the picosecond laser and detection equipment is given. The argon ion laser (Coherent Radiation model CR18UV) was mode-locked using a Brewster cut acoustic-optic prism (Harris) driven by a radio frequency (RF) source stabilized with a digital synchronizer (Marconi model TF 2173). For all the experiments described the 457.9 nm laser line was used. The output power of the laser was 400 mW continuous wave at 30A plasma tube discharge current, and after mode-locking the average power was 110 mW. This yields a peak power of about 15 W with a full width at half maximum (FWHM) of the light pulses of about 100 ps. The mode-locking frequency was 38.080 MHz, the pulse repetition rate was 76.160 MHz. The shape of the mode-locked light pulses was continuously monitored using a home-built fast detector (Telefunken type BPW28 photo-diode[6]) and a sampling oscilloscope (Hewlett Packard model 1430 C, 1811 A and 182 C, rise time approximately 20 ps). With the relatively simple detector mount (version A[6]) rise times of less than 100 ps FWHM were registered although these were detector-limited (> 300 ps FWHM). Nevertheless we regard the displayed pulse shapes as sufficient criterion for obtaining optimum mode-locking. The final fine adjustments could be performed

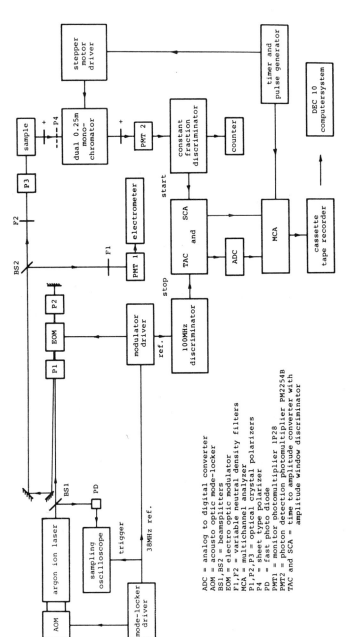

ADC = analog to digital converter
AOM = acousto optic mode-locker
BS1,BS2 = beamsplitters
EOM = electro optic modulator
F1,F2 = variable neutral density filters
MCA = multichannel analyzer
P1,P2,P3 = optical crystal polarizers
P4 = sheet type polarizer
PD = fast photo diode
PMT1 = monitor photomultiplier 1P28
PMT2 = photon detection photomultiplier PM2254B
TAC and SCA = time to amplitude converter with
              amplitude window discriminator

Figure 1

*Schematic diagram of the picosecond laser apparatus for measurement of
fluorescence decay kinetics and time-resolved fluorescence emission spectra
using single photon counting detection. For some measurements the dual monochromator was replaced by a Schott RG665 cut-off filter.*

using data from the time resolved photon counting equipment, which can give information over a much wider dynamic range than the photodiode.

In order to prevent triplet state build-up in the samples, the repetition rate of the light pulses was reduced to 297.5 kHz or 74.375 kHz ($\div 2^8$ and $\div 2^{10}$) using an electro-optic modulator set-up as described previously[7]. To improve the contrast ratio between suppressed and transmitted light pulses (down to 1/100,000) a dual-pass arrangement was used. The modulator action was continuously monitored via a beam-splitter using a standard photomultiplier (1P28) and an electrometer (Keithley model 610c). The light flux to this monitor was controlled using reflecting neutral density filters (Balzers), and these were also used to check the linearity of the monitor system. After modulation the light pulses had peak powers of less than 4 W and average powers were about 50μW. This was sufficient to measure the short (∿50ps) lifetimes from weakly emitting chlorophyll-proteins. Fluorescence emission was detected perpendicular to the excitation beam and focussed on the input slit of a dual 0.25m monochromator set (Jarrell Ash, 2 x model 82-410). In front of the input slit was placed a sheet polarizer, rotated 54.7⁰ with respect to the vertical direction of excitation polarization in order to minimize any effects of rotational motion on the lifetimes[8]. The emission was then focussed on the cathode of the photomultiplier (Philips PM 2254B) using a laboratory-built floating lens adapter and vacuum window optics in the thermo-electrically cooled photomultiplier housing (Products for Research model TE 104 RF).

The anode current pulses from single photon events
at the cathode of the photomultiplier were analyzed
using a constant fraction discriminator (CFD, Canberra
model 1428A). The count rate of the photons was
continuously monitored using a counter (Hewlett Packard
model 5328A). Standard negative logic pulses from the
CFD were used to start the time-to-amplitude converter
(TAC, Canberra Time Analyzer model 2043). The TAC was
stopped via a 100 MHz discriminator (Ortec model 436)
using the same reference frequency as used to trigger the
modulator driver. The TAC was equipped with a single
channel analyzer, so that analogue output pulses could be
discriminated. When an output pulse height was between
a chosen lower and upper level (Time and Δ Time controls
on the TAC) a logic pulse was generated. These logic
pulses were used to record a time resolved wavelength
spectrum with the multichannel analyzer (MCA, Laben model
8001) in a multichannel scaling (MCS) mode, the channels
stepping synchronously with the monochromator wavelength
drive (laboratory built timer and pulse generator). In
order to record a fluorescence decay, the analogue output
pulses from the TAC were analyzed with the analogue-to-
digital converter (ADC, Laben model 8212) and stored in
the MCA in pulse height analysis (PHA) mode.

For fluorescence anisotropy measurements, the sheet
polarizer P4 and the monochromators were replaced by
a rotatable polarization analyzer (Glan Thompson type)
and the stepper motor driver was replaced by a

laboratory built rotator driver. The wavelength of the
fluorescence emission was selected using a Schott cut-off
filter (RG 665 usually). The memory of the MCA was divided
into two halves, one registering the emission polarised
parallel to the polarisation of the excitation beam ($I_{||}$),
the other the emission polarised perpendicular ($I_\perp$). The
polarization analyzer and the MCA were driven by the MCA
timer (Laben model 8190) to execute the sequence: measurement
of parallel polarized emission during 10 seconds, rotate the
polarizer 90°, measure perpendicular polarized emission
during 10 seconds, and finally rotate the polarizer to
original orientation. This cycle was usually repeated for
5-20 times. The data was transferred to the DEC 10 computer
via a cassette tape recorder (Racal model PI 72) for
analysis by an iterative least-squares fit programme which
convolutes up to three exponential components with the
instrument response function. Recently we have made data
collection and transfer to the DEC-10 more convenient by
replacement of the Laben MCA with a Nuclear Data 66 MCA/
terminal.

The frequency of photon detection (= start frequency) was
set to be 5% of the frequency of the excitation pulses
(= stop frequency) by attenuating the excitation light with
neutral density filters (Balzer). The pulse pile-up
distortion[9] was then less than distortion from other sources.
Another source of distortion was the presence of coherent or
synchronous electro-magnetic interference that contributes
to oscillation-like signals superimposed on the decay curves.

This interference was caused by firing the modulator driver[7] or triggering the discriminators, producing fast electromagnetic spikes. These spikes caused small signals in the 50 ohms coax cables connecting the different parts of the start-stop equipment, and leading to an error in the timing discrimination. It is even possible that the linear ramp signal inside the TAC was slightly distorted directly. In this manner the statistics of the measurement could be influenced in a way that we can still only partly understand. An example of the distortions occuring within the TAC are those caused by the non-random stop repetition rate when the TAC was started with pulses from discriminated photon events (a complex Poisson distribution) and stopped with the much higher, but constant, repetition rate of the light flashes. This source of distortion could however be eliminated by using a gate in the path of the stop pulses (see reference 10), but our experience is that this source of distortion is certainly not the most important one. We find that the best solution is to locate empirically that time window for the TAC (by varying the delays in the start and the stop chain of the apparatus), which shows the minimum distortion. This time-consuming procedure has to be repeated if adjustments are made for instance in the timescale of the TAC. The distortions could in principle be corrected for by dividing the experimental curve by a correction curve obtained at the end of a series of measurements. Uncorrelated photons from the room lighting (laser closed) were used to start the TAC, and by adjusting the opening of the shutter to the sample housing the frequency of the photons could be chosen to be the same as used in the fluorescence decay experiments. The so-called correction curve should be an equal distribution of counts over the different channels of the MCA, however variations between the contents of the channels of the MCA arise due to normal statistical variation and also to the oscillation-like distortion. To make the statistical distribution small compared to the distortion effects, up to about 10,000 counts per channel were needed, requiring several hours counting. Correction for this distortion is not necessary for anisotropy measurements: $r(t) = (I_{||} - I_{\perp})/(I_{||} + 2I_{\perp})$[11]. In figure 2 an example is given of a typical correction curve together with the deviation functions for corrected and uncorrected fluorescence decay curves. In this case, although some slight gain in the quality of fit is obtained after correction, the effect is rather marginal: the oscillations remain to some extent superimposed on a noisy straight line centered on zero deviation. The computed values of the lifetime before and after correction are identical within experimental error. It is important to realise that pronounced distortions in the decay curve at short times after the pulse may make it impossible to resolve short components with rate constants similar to those defining the distortion.

Another important source of artefacts can be the wavelength dependency of the transit time of photoelectrons in

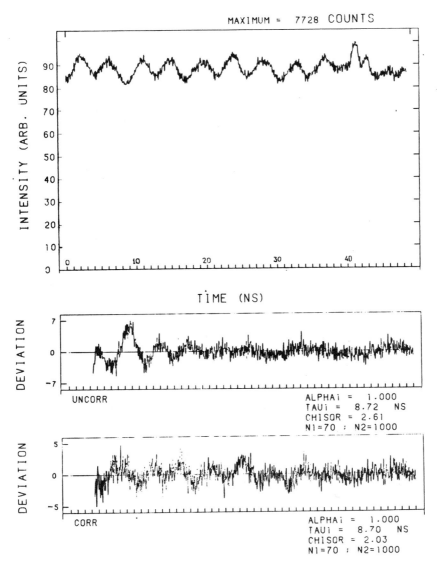

Figure 2

An example of a correction curve, together with plots of the deviation from fitted decay kinetics (after convolution with the instrumental response function) for the uncorrected experimental results (uncorr.) and after correction with the correction curve(corr.).

the photomultiplier. The finite duration of the exciting
pulse as detected by the time-resolved photon counting
equipment (about 500 ps FWHM) requires the use of
deconvolution procedures for the extraction of short
decay times from the experimental data: we use a non-
linear least-squares method for that purpose[12]. The
instrumental response function of the detection chain was
measured using scattered laser light from a small piece
of quartz rod in the sample compartment. This 'excitation
pulse' curve was measured at the same photon detection
rate as used for the fluorescence decay measurements.
Broadening of the pulse detected in this way compared to
the 100 ps FWHM of the Ar^+ laser pulse was mainly caused by
transit time fluctuations in the photomultiplier[13, 14].
The time resolution of the system can be greatly increased
by using photomultipliers with a microchannel-plate
electron muliplier[15-18]. To check the wavelength
dependency of the temporal response of the detection
chain, the fluorescence decay kinetics of a test sample
with a known short fluorescence lifetime, which absorbed
and emitted in the same wavelength region as the
chlorophyll proteins, was also measured.

For this purpose a solution of erythrosine B in water
was used. The lifetime measured was 88 ± 10 ps, in close
agreement with earlier reported values (90,110 and 57 ps,
see reference 19). When a small synthetic shift in time
was applied to fluorescence data with respect to the
instrumental response function, it was not found possible

to improve the quality of the fit. Our conclusion is that the wavelength dependency of the transit time of the photomultiplier used (Philips type PM 2254B, S20 photocathode sensitivity characteristic and quartz window) must be negligible on this timescale. Earlier we have reported this same check procedure for another photomultiplier, the Philips XP 2020[20].

Measuring fluorescence lifetimes as short as those reported here ($\sim$ 40 ps) requires from the equipment a high degree of stability and reproducability. In order to provide the stop signal to the TAC an electronic reference signal was used, which was generated by electronically dividing the mode-locking frequency of the mode-locker driver[7]. Depending on the long term temperature stability in the room (20 $\pm$ 1°C) a slow shift of the mode-locked light pulses with respect to the mode-locker drive signal, up to several picoseconds per hour, could be observed. Gathering data necessary for an anisotropy measurement (including rotation of the polarization analyzer) required up to several minutes. For such lengthy measurement periods it might be expected that greater stability would be obtained by using the light pulse (via a fast photodiode and a CFD) to stop the TAC. We have attempted this, hoping that the instrumental response function would be additionally improved by avoiding the short-term time jitter between mode-locked light pulses and modelocker drive signal. However, hardly any improvement in time response could be observed. Our conclusion was that the instrumental response function is mainly determined by the detection chain. We believe that the photomultiplier is the main factor in increasing the FWHM of the instrumental response function. Careful focussing of the fluorescence on the photocathode and optimisation of the electro-statical focussing between the accelerating electrodes of the electron multiplier would certainly help[14]. We routinely use the electronic reference signal from the modulator driver to stop the TAC, accepting the very small long term shift in time between electronic reference and light pulses, rather than use the fast photodiode.

iii) FDMR

In figure 3 a schematic diagram of the FDMR-apparatus is given. The excitation source was a Coherent Radiation model CR4 continuous wave argon ion laser. In all the experiments described the 457.9 nm line was used to excite the samples. The equipment as depicted in figure 3 is a multi-purpose set-up, on which fluorescence fading (FF) experiments can also be performed.

Via a small mirror the laser beam was deflected towards a quartz rod (Suprasil 1, 1m x 5mm Ø) through a lens which was used to collimate the sample fluorescence emission appearing from the upper surface of the quartz rod. The rod was inserted into a liquid helium Dewar with the sample at the lower end of the rod in a plastic cup. The cup was surrounded by a microwave helix of enamelled copper wire. The emission was focussed on the

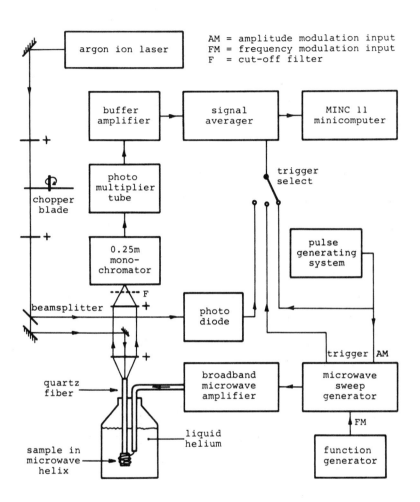

Figure 3

Schematic diagram of the FDMR apparatus. For details see text.

input slit of a monochromator (Spex Minimate, f = 0.25m)
using a lens similar to the collimating lens (Suprasil 1,
f = 50mm). A wavelength selection filter, in this case a
Schott OG 590 cut-off filter, was placed in front of the
input slit. The output from the monochromator was focussed
onto the cathode of the photomultiplier (RCA type C31034A)
using a floating lens adaptor (Spex model 1630 A3) and vacuum
window optics in the thermo-electrically cooled photomultiplier housing (Products for Research model TE104 RF).
The anode current of the photomultiplier (maximum 100 nA)
was amplified using a laboratory-built buffer amplifier
yielding a voltage gain of 10x and either a 1MΩ or a 100 kΩ
impedance at the anode, and giving a possible minimum
detectable rise time with the given parasitic capacitances
of better than 0.1 ms (RC $\overset{\sim}{\sim}$ 25.10^{-6}s). For FDMR work the
higher anode impedance (1MΩ) was usually chosen. The
output of the buffer amplifier was fed to the input of the
signal averager (PAR model 4203) or for preliminary
adjustments to a Yt-recorder. The transfer of data from the
averager to the laboratory minicomputer (MINC) was via a
general purpose interface bus (IEEE488).

For FDMR spectra illumination was continuous (chopper
blade kept stationary), and after optimization of the
optical excitation and detection chain the exciting power
was chosen (Balzers reflecting neutral density filters) to
yield a triplet population of <10% as measured by the
fluorescence fading technique (see later). The high
voltage on the photomultiplier (power supply: Fluke model

412 B) was adjusted to give an anode current of 100 nA
at the chosen detection wavelength (650-750 nm) and
bandwidth (usually 5 nm). At the output of the buffer
amplifier an extra capacitance (usually 1 µF) was added
as an anti-aliasing filter, the signal was AC-coupled
to the averager. The microwave sweep generator (Hewlett
Packard model 8620 C with model 86220 A RF plug-in) was
set to produce a repetitive linear frequency sweep over
a chosen range, with the averager triggered synchronously
at the beginning of each sweep. In this mode amplitude
modulation (AM) and frequency modulation (FM) of the
sweep generator were not used. The signal output of the
sweep generator was fed to the microwave helix via a 27
dB broadband amplifier (Minicircuits model ZHL 2-12).
With the equipment used as described, the exciting
microwave frequency was usually swept through the spectrum
between 10 MHz and 1300 MHz in 1 sec. The principle of
FDMR measurements is reviewed fully in reference 2. In
general, the three triplet spinlevels are non-degenerate
and are separated by the so-called zero-field splittings,
which can be expressed as D+E, D-E, and 2E (in energy
units), where D and E measure the triplet dipolar spin-
spin interaction   Briefly, when the microwave frequency
is such that $h\nu$ fits one of the three energy gaps between
the three triplet state spin levels ($1x>$, $1y>$, and $1z>$),
the populations of these two spin levels will be equalised
if sufficient microwave power is applied. This can result
in a change in the total triplet state population and
thus a change in the singlet state population (S_0),

which in turn affects the yield of emission from S_1. An example of the effect of resonance between spin levels on chlorophyll fluorescence in a chlorophyll protein is given in figure 4a. Because of the relatively small changes in singlet population ($\Delta F/F$ is about 0.1%) the noise from excitation fluctuations and fluorescence photon statistics is dominant and the signal from many sweeps must be averaged in order to obtain a reasonable signal to noise ratio (S/N>5): 100-2000 microwave frequency sweeps for a typical chlorophyll-protein. It will be clear that one has to be very careful of artefacts generated by synchronous noise when so many sweeps are used for averaging. The reproducibility of the calibration system of the microwave frequency in the FDMR spectra as gathered in the signal averager was better than ±15MHz. This reproducibility was limited by the properties of the microwave sweep generator when calibrating the resonance frequencies in the experimentally recorded spectrum using a Syntron Donner model 1017 + 1292 A plug-in microwave counter with the generator operated in the continuous wave mode and aligning the markers of the generator with the peaks in the recorded spectrum.

The equipment shown in figure 3 can also be used for FDMR kinetic measurements, yielding the decay rate constants of the three triplet spin levels (see legend to figure 4c). The microwave frequency was set at one specific value resonant with one of the energy gaps between the triplet spin levels. The illumination was continuous but an on/off switching sequence was applied to the microwave power using the pulse generating system (Farnell) via the AM input of the microwave generator. The period of the on/off switching had to be chosen to allow the system to reach a steady state after switching the microwave power, and this is largely determined by the slowest triplet spin level decay rate constant. For our samples $k_z \sim 100$ s^{-1}, and an on/off cycle of 100 ms was chosen (50% on/50% off). Further, in order to obtain undistorted kinetics it is important to saturate the transition instantaneously (microwave powers 500-800 mW at least are needed) and regulate the light intensity with neutral density filters to restrict the triplet population to a maximum of about 10%[21]. Under these experimental conditions it was necessary to average the signal from 50,000 - 200,000 on/off cycles to obtain an acceptable signal to noise ratio (S/N >5). On applying microwave power a selective equalization of the populations of two triplet spin levels was obtained, and the kinetics of the change in intensity of fluorescence at a chosen wavelength and bandwidth was a function of the decay rate constants of these triplet spin levels[21]. An example of FDMR kinetics is given in Figure 4c. For synchronization, the signal averager was triggered with the same rectangular pulse train as the AM input of the microwave generator. In order to increase the S/N ratio the microwave frequency could be modulated over the frequency range of the FDMR signal (FWHM $\sim$30 MHz). For this purpose a 50 kHz modulation rate over $\pm$ 15 MHz range

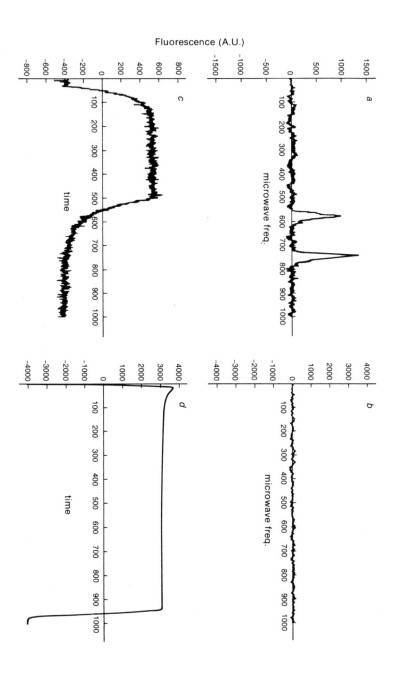

Figure 4a

The FDMR spectrum of Chla-P1 at 4.2K. Excitation wavelength 458nm, excitation intensity about 50 mW. Emission wavelength 718nm (bandwidth 5nm). Microwave power 500 mW, sweep rate 1300 MHz/s. Frequency of transition centres: D-E, 737 Mhz and D + E, 968 MHz. Number of microwave sweeps: 1000. On the frequency scale one unit corresponds to 1.39 MHz.

Figure 4b

The FDMR spectrum of Chl_a-P1 at 4.2K after oxidation of P700 with 1mM ferricyanide/ferrocyanide (100:1) in 10 mM phosphate buffer pH 6.8 for 30 min. at $0°C$ in the dark. The gel piece was suspended in excess of this medium (100ml) and continuously stirred during this period. Other conditions the same as for (a).

Figure 4c

The FDMR kinetics of Chl_a-P1 at 4.2K. Excitation wavelength 458 nm, excitation power 14 mW. Emission wavelength 718 nm (5 nm bandwidth). Switched microwave power 800 mW, switching cycle 50 ms on/50 ms off. The frequency was modulated at 50 kHz over the range 735 ± 15 MHz (D-E transition). The photomultiplier anode impedance was 1 MΩ (RC time about $750S^{-1}$). The experimental time was over 6 hours (230700 switching cycles). The rise in fluorescence is described by $\exp[(-k_y + k_z)t/2]$ and the fall by $(k_y)^{-1}\exp(-k_yt) - (k_z)^{-1}\exp(-k_zt)$ (reference 21). Analysis of the curve using these expressions results in $k_y = 288 \pm 110 \text{ s}^{-1}$, $k_z = 128 \pm 24 \text{ s}^{-1}$. On the time scale one unit corresponds to 0.1 ms.

Figure 4d

The FF spectrum of Chl_a-P1 at 4.2K. Excitation wavelength 458 nm, excitation power about 40 mW. Emission wavelength 718 nm. Light-on period about 40 ms. Number of accumulated light block pulses: 10 000. The decrease in fluorescence ($\Delta F/F$) = 0.09, and is described by the sum of three exponentials with rate constants $k_1 = 2133 \pm 300$, $k_2 = 552 \pm 17$, $k_3 = 93 \pm 6 \text{ s}^{-1}$; and coefficients $\alpha_1 = 0.11$, $\alpha_2 = 0.71$ and $\alpha_3 = 0.18$. On the time scale one unit corresponds to 40 microsec.

was applied using a function generator (Wavetek model 185) via the FM input. Excitation of the inhomogeneously broadened FDMR-signal may give signal enhancement but it also averages the FDMR kinetics over the range of species within the FDMR peak and may also make 'instaneous' saturation with microwave power more difficult. In this way we can measure the rate constants of two spinlevels of selected triplets, but it requires several hours experimental time for each measurement.

This is in contrast to the Fluorescence Fading (FF) technique in which all the rate constants of the spin levels of all the different triplet states present are observed non-selectively[4].

For FF experiments the same apparatus shown in figure 3 was used. The microwave power source was not required. The response of the fluorescence intensity of the sample to a light blockpulse was measured and the grow-in of the fluorescence and its subsequent fading over a chosen period was averaged (see figure 4d). The laboratory-built chopper blade was rotated using a function generator and an amplifier. The fluorescence signal was synchronously recorded on the PAR model 4203 signal averager, which was triggered on the rising flank of the light pulse block via a beamsplitter and photodiode (EG & G type DT25, battery powered). The time resolution of the apparatus was determined by the speed of the chopper blade and the diameter of the light beam at the chopper blade.

To allow measurement of rate constants as fast as
$k \sim 10,000$ s^{-1} positive 10 cm focal length lenses were
used to focus the laser beam at the chopper blade. The
rotation time of the blade was chosen to be as short as
possible whilst still allowing sufficient of the slow
component ($k \sim 100$ s^{-1}) to be seen in the light-on period
to be able to predict the true steady state with sufficient
precision, and also allowing a complete relaxation to the
ground state within the dark period between light block
pulses. Recently we have replaced the chopper blade by
an acousto-optic modulator to allow greater freedom in
the choice of light and dark periods. As with FDMR kinetics
it is necessary to restrict the triplet state population
to < 10% in order to prevent an artefactual increase in
the measured decay rate constants. The great advantage
of the FF technique compared to FDMR kinetics is that the
individual decay rate constants, and the relative population
levels and population rates of the triplet state spin
levels can all be determined in one experiment. Also, it
is relatively simple to obtain excellent signal to noise
ratios (S/N > 100) by averaging the signal from 10,000 -
50,000 light blockpulses within an experimental time of
10 - 100 min. As with FDMR kinetics the fluorescence
fading technique is highly sensitive to distortion due
to coherent noise. The curves obtained in FDMR kinetics
and FF are analysed for up to three exponential components
using an iterative least-squares fit procedure. The
decay rate constants are dependent on excitation light

intensity and the true rate constants are found by

extrapolating the measured values to zero excitation intensity.

Results and Discussion

In all experiments using picosecond pulses to excite chlorophyll-proteins at room temperature it is important to use low excitation powers ($<10^{10}$ -10^{11}/cm^2/pulse) and to choose an interpulse interval long enough to allow relaxation to the groundstate between pulses[1]. In Table I the major fluorescence decay component of Chl$_a$-P1 is seen to be as short as 40 ps for this sodium-dedecyl sulphate-prepared chlorophyll-protein at room temperature. We have shown that using adequate calibration and reference techniques that the time-resolved single photon counting method is able to measure lifetimes down to several tens of ps to an accuracy of about 15%. However we have not yet investigated decay profiles made up of several components having similar short lifetimes. Less than 10^7 excitation pulses, with energies down to 10^{-11} J (at 458 nm) over an experimental period of several min. were sufficient to determine fluorescence lifetimes with sufficient accuracy. In the chlorophyll-proteins studied it was not possible to detect any fluorescence anisotropy, as might be expected if subpicosecond energy transfer takes place between non-ordered chlorophylls within the protein molecule. As shown for Chl$_{ab}$ -P2 in figure 5 we are able to accumulate up to 100 000 counts per channel in the maximum, at a photon detection rate of 15 kHz, and observe the decay over about three decades. Promising developments[15-18] concerning photo-multipliers having microchannel plate electron multipliers,

Table 1. Fluorescence decay kinetics of Chl_a-P1 at 293K [a), c)]

Detection wavelength [b)] (nm)	α_1	τ_1(ps)	α_2	τ_2(ns)	α_3	τ_3(ns)
>665	0.93±0.03	41±8	0.06±0.02	1.14±0.17	0.017±0.004	5.8±1.7
715	0.977	39	0.013	1.84	0.010	5.61
670	0.616	369	0.384	4.27		

a) $I(t) = I(O) \left[\alpha_1 exp(-t/\tau_1) + \alpha_2 exp(-t/\tau_2) + \alpha_3 exp(-t/\tau_3) \right]$

b) For λ_f >665nm a Schott RG665 cut-off wavelength selection filter was used. For 715 and 670nm measurements a monochromator (bandwidth 4nm) was used: these measurements were on a partially denatured sample.

c) The value of χ^2 for these measurements was 1.2-2.9.

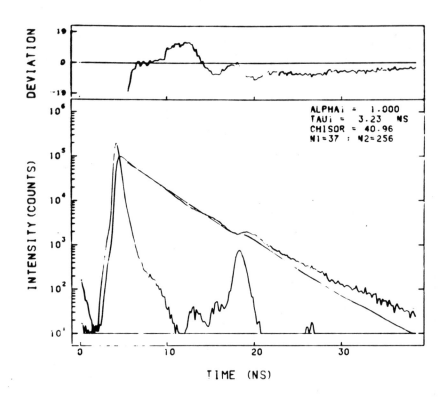

Figure 5

*The fluorescence decay kinetics of Chl_{ab}^-P2 at 293 K.
The experimentally found emission response (emission
wavelengths > 665 nm, Schott RG665 cut-off filter) is
fitted to either one, or two, exponential components
convoluted with the instrumental response function.
The residual oscillatory deviation could not be removed*

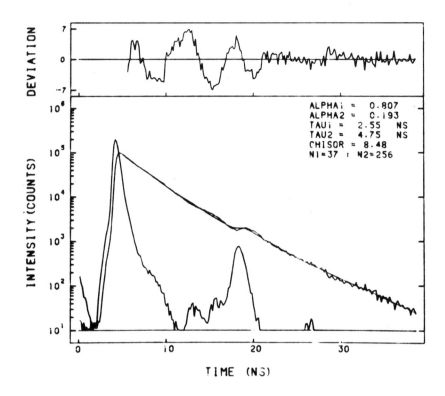

by the correction procedure described in the text. Time
per MCA channel: 0.1504 ns. Interpulse interval 3 μs.
Photon detection rate 15 kHz. The smaller pulse after
about 15 ns is characteristic of this type of photomultiplier and is due to a deviation from the normal path
of a part of the photoelectrons within the photomultiplier.

which can reduce the transit time jitter of photon events
down to several tens of ps, may allow better detection of
events even faster than 40 ps in the future. One major
problem which still remains is the distortion of the
detected fluorescence decay profile probably due to a
sum of oscillatory interferences (see figure 2). It has
not been possible to correct completely for this distortion
using the correction curve procedure described, although
this procedure can help to reduce the χ^2-value. A more
effective way for elimination of this distortion would be
valuable.

The photosystem I reaction centre protein Chl_a-Pl shows
a very short fluorescence lifetime of the antenna
chlorophyll (about 40 Chl *a* per P700) which we attribute
to rapid energy transfer to an active reaction centre.
The 40 ps component is seen in the total emission band of
the native protein at room temperature, and also at longer
wavelengths (e.g 714 nm) even after partial denaturation
(see Table I). The FDMR spectrum shown in figure 4a is
constant for all emission wavelengths above 701 nm and
we suggest that this represents the FDMR spectrum of
P700 (primary donor) Chl *a* seen in the emission from
low-energy traps within the antenna bed emitting with
high yield at 4.2K[22],

It is inverted (an increase in fluorescence on
resonance with the microwave frequency) compared to FDMR
spectra seen at emission wavelengths shorter than

701 nm[2,3,22]. This interpretation can also explain the apparently anomalous relative population levels of the triplet spin levels obtained from FF experiments such as shown in figure 4d. From these relative populations one would predict an FDMR spectrum with negative sign (a decrease in fluorescence on resonance with microwaves), but subsequently the sign is reversed on energy transfer from the bulk antenna to the low energy traps within the antenna bed[22,23].

Figure 4b shows that oxidation of P700 with a redox buffer of E = + 550 mV leads to the disappearance of the FDMR spectrum, consistent with the requirement for active photochemistry in the reaction centre for observation of the reaction centre chlorophyll triplet state. It appears that this triplet is formed by the radical pair mechanism (see for example reference 24), and this process has been discussed elsewhere[22]. FDMR kinetics of Chl_a-Pl, such as that shown in figure 4c, have been measured in order to support the measurements of triplet state spin level decay rate constants using the FF technique (figure 4d). FDMR kinetics can give information about one particular triplet with a pronounced FDMR spectrum in the presence of a heterogenous population of triplet states not detectable by FDMR. However, to date the decay rate constants measured have proved to be anomalously low, probably as a result of insufficient microwave power (800 mW is the maximum available to us at present).

The 293K Chl a fluorescence decay kinetics of Chl_{ab}-P2 measured in situ in electrophoresis gel is best fitted by two components: a major ($A_1 \approx 0.8$) 2.5 ns component and a 4.7 ns component ($A_2 \approx 0.2$). Lotshaw et al[25] have also recently reported this unexpectedly complex emission kinetics of monomeric Chl_{ab} protein. The minor light-harvesting Chl_{ab}-P1 also shows similar emission kinetics in the native state but with slightly less 2.5 ns component ($A_1 \approx 0.7$). The fluorescence lifetimes are sensitive to partial denaturation: illumination at 293K for periods of >15 min leads to a shortening of both components. In order to define the interactions between chl in Chl_{ab}-P2 which lead to two distinguishable chl a species we have used the Fluorescence Detected Magnetic Resonance (FDMR) technique to study chl triplet states at 4.2K[26]. Chl_{ab}-P2 excited in the chl b Soretband (476 nm) shows a narrow (< 10 MHz) 2E transition in the chl a emission band which is lost on partial (1 min, 100°C) denaturation, and which is not seen for chl a in vitro. This, and the narrowness of the 2E transition compared to the D-E and D+E transitions, appear to indicate a chl a with a unique interaction with chl b, together with a more heterogeneous chl a triplet state population within the Chl_{ab}-P2 molecule (about 5 chl a, 4 chl b per 33kD).

The picosecond laser apparatus shown in figure 1 has also been used to obtain room temperature emission spectra from chlorophyll-proteins, and the emission maximum for native Chl_{ab}-P2 was found to be 686 nm, shifting to shorter wavelengths (678-680 nm) on partial denaturation[26]. This, together with the lifetime and FDMR data has lead us to propose a model for Chl_{ab}-P2 in which two types of chl *a* exist: that which is relatively 'isolated', and that which is closely associated with chl *b* in a more or less unique way, and having an increased rate of intersystem crossing and a shorter fluorescence lifetime[26].

Acknowledgements

The authors are indebted to Dr A.J.W.G. Visser, who - together with Ing A. van Hoek - was responsible for the initial development of the laser set-up described. We also acknowledge Drs L. Benthem and Dr. G.H. van Brakel for useful discussions on the FDMR and FF measurements. The chlorophyll-proteins were made available by Prof D. von Wettstein and Dr B.L. Møller of the Carlsberg Laboratory through a joint project supported by the Commission of the European Communities (contract ESD-O13-DK(G)). This research was supported by the Netherlands Foundation for Chemical Research (SON) with financial aid from the Netherlands Organisation for the Advancement of Pure Research (ZWO).

References

1. G.S. Beddard, G.R. Fleming, G.Porter, G.F.W. Searle
    and J.A. Synowiec (1979). *Biochim.Biophys.Acta*
    545, 165-174.

2. T.J. Schaafsma (1982). *ODMR, techniques and application
    to biophysics (ed*. R.H. Clarke) Wiley, New York,
    291-365.

3. G.F.W. Searle, R.B. M. Koehorst, T.J. Schaafsma,
    B.L. Møller and D. von Wettstein (1981). *Carlsberg
    Res. Commun*. **46**, 183-194.

4. R. Avarmaa (1977). *Chem. Phys. Lett*. **46**, 279-282.

5. O. Machold, D.J. Simpson and B.L. Møller (1979).
    Carlsberg Res. Commun. **44**, 235-254.

6. D. Bebelaar (1979). *Rev. Sci. Instrum*. **50**, 1629-1633.

7. A. van Hoek and A.J.W.G. Visser (1981). *Rev. Sci.
    Instrum*. **52**, 1199-1205.

8. R.D. Spencer and G. Weber (1970). *J.Chem.Phys*. **52**,
    1654-1663.

9. C.M. Harris and B.K. Selinger (1979). *Aust.J.Chem*. **32**,
    2111-2129.

10. W. Hachnel, J.A. Nairn, P. Reisberg and K. Sauer (1982).
    Biochim.Biophys. Acta **680**, 161-173.

11. R.E.Dale, L.A. Chen and L. Brand (1976). *Biophys J*.
    16, 571-583.

12. A. Grinvald and I.Z. Steinberg (1974). *Anal. Biochem*.
    59, 583-598.

13. Ph. Wahl, J.C. Auchet and B. Douzel (1974). *Rev.Sci.
    Instrum*. **45**, 28-32.

14. D.Bebelaar. Private communication.

15. C.C.Lo and B. Leskovar (1981). *I.E.E.E. Trans. Nucl.Sci*. NS-28, 698-704.

16. I. Yamazaki, T. Murao and K. Yoshihara (1982). *Chem.Phys.Lett*. 87,384-388.

17. T. Murao, I. Yamazaki and K. Yoshihara (1982). *Appl.Opt*. 21, 2297-2298.

18. R.W. Wijnaendts van Resandt, R.H. Vogel and S.W.Provencher (1982). *Rev.Sci.Instrum*. 53, 1392-1397.

19. K.B. Eisenthal (1977). *Annu.Rev.Phys.Chem*. 28, 207-232.

20. A.J.W.G. Visser and A. van Hoek (1979). *J.Biochem. Biophys.Methods I,* 195-208.

21. S.J. van der Bent (1977). *Thesis,* Wageningen.

22. G.F.W. Searle, A.van Hoek, T.J. Schaafsma, B.L. Møller and D.von Wettstein (1983) in preparation.

23. G.H. van Brakel, G.F.W. Searle, and T.J. Schaafsma (1983), in preparation.

24. R.E.Blankenship (1981). *Acc.Chem.Res*. 14, 163-170.

25. W.T. Lotshaw, R.S. Alberte and G.R. Fleming (1982), *Biochim.Biophys.Acta* 682, 75-85.

26. G.F.W. Searle, H. Fraaije, T.J. Schaafsma, B.L. Møller and D. von Wettstein (1983) in preparation.

Time-Resolved Fluorescence Spectroscopic Study of Lipid Motion in Biological Membranes

C.D. Stubbs[*+o], K. Kinosita[*], Jr., F.Munkonge[+], P.J. Quinn[+] and A. Ikegami[*]

* *The Institute of Physical and Chemical Research, Hirosawa, Wakoshi, Saitama, Japan*

+ *Chelsea College, Manresa Road, London SW3*

o *Present address: The Royal Institution, 21, Albemarle Street, London W1X 4BS*

Introduction

A major approach to the understanding of the functional properties of biological membranes has been the use of extrinsic fluorescent probes to examine the motional properties of the lipid region. 1,6-diphenyl-1,3,5-hexatriene (DPH) has been particularly useful in this respect due to its favourable fluorescence properties[1]. Time-resolved fluorescence anisotropy measurements of DPH[2,3,4] can yield both orientational (rotational *range* of motion) and dynamic (*rate* of motion) parameters. Such studies have yielded information on lipid phase transitions[2,3,4], effects of cholesterol[5,6], fatty acyl unsaturation[7] and protein-lipid interactions in membranes[8,9].

The protein-lipid interfacial region is of particular interest since it is in this region where many of the modulatory effects of membrane lipids on membrane proteins (as enzymes, receptors or transport systems) are likely to be exerted. Time-resolved studies with DPH have been performed on cytochrome oxidase[8], and sarcoplasmic reticulum, erythrocyte, mitochondrial and purple membranes[9]. The general conclusions have been that the presence of protein severely limits the angular range of motion and decreases the rate of motion of the DPH molecule, and by inference the fatty acyl chains of the membrane phospholipids, in the protein-lipid interfacial region.

If the range of motion, measured as the cone angle (see below) is used to calculate an order parameter, S, then the effect of protein is to increase S. However, the order parameter calculated from ^2H NMR measurements on deuterated fatty acyl chains of phospholipids reveal the opposite effect: protein decreases S[10]. It has been suggested that as the DPH molecule is rigid its motion would be insensitive to minute irregularities on the protein surface into which it could not penetrate[10,11,12]

However, the more flexible deuterated fatty acyl chain would detect these irregularities. Furthermore fitting into the irregular protein surface would cause considerable deflection of the $C - {}^2H$ bond with respect to the bilayer normal thus decreasing S. The DPH order parameter is calculated without reference to the bilayer normal and the restricted motion due to either the

inflexible protein wall or grooves in it, able to accommodate
the DPH, would increase the order parameter.

Reconciliation of the ^{2}H NMR and DPH results can be made
also, partly on the basis of the different time regimes
sensed (10^{-5} sec and 10^{-8} -10^{-9} sec respectively). It has
been suggested[12] that while in ^{2}H-NMR a 'total orientational
order parameter' is detected, DPH detects a 'rigid-body order'
of the fatty acyl chains and not some types of the conformational disorder detected by ^{2}H-NMR.

One of the problems with DPH is that its precise location
in the lipid bilayer is not known although there is evidence
that it orients roughly parallel to the fatty acyl chains
and in the middle of the bilayer[13].

In this study we have used DPH and also 1-(4-trimethy-
ammoniumphenyl)-6-phenyl-1,3,5-hexatriene (TMA-DPH) and
1-acyl, 2-(DPH)-phosphatidylcholine (DPH-PC), with more
precisely known locations in the lipid bilayer, in an attempt
to further understanding of lipid motional characteristics in
the protein-lipid interfacial region, using skeletal muscle
sarcoplasmic reticulum (SR) membranes.

Materials and Methods
Rabbit white skeletal muscle sarcoplasmic reticulum was
prepared according to Warren *et al*[14]. DPH and TMA-DPH were
obtained from Molecular Probes Inc. DPH-PC, prepared from

egg yolk lysophosphatidylcholine acylated with 4-(2-carboxyethyl)-DPH[15], was kindly provided by Professor R.B. Cundall. The probes were dissolved in tetrahydrofuran (DPH) or ethanol (TMA-DPH, DPH-PC). Fatty acids were obtained from Sigma.

Probes and fatty acids were incorporated into SR membranes by addition in solvent to a membrane suspension in 0.05M phosphate buffer (pH 7.4) and incubation for 30 min. Multilamellar liposomes, prepared from total lipid extracts[16], were prepared with the required amount of probe and fatty acid as previously described.

Decays of fluorescence anisotropy and total fluorescence intensity were measured on a single photon counting fluorimeter[17], incorporating various modifications[9].

The steady state fluorescence anisotropy was calculated according the relationship:

$$r^s = \frac{I_V - GI_H}{I_V + 2GI_H} \qquad \ldots (1)$$

where G is the ratio of the sensitivities of the detection system for vertically and horizontally polarized light, taken to be I_V/I_H obtained with horizontally polarized excitation. The fluorescence decay data were analyzed by assuming exponential decays of the following forms:

$$I_{T} \delta (t) = \alpha_1 \exp (-t/\tau_1) + \alpha_1 \exp (-t/\tau_2) \qquad ...(2)$$

$$r^{S} (t) = (r_{o} - r_{\infty}) \exp (-t/\phi) + r_{\infty} \qquad ...(3)$$

where the subscript δ indicates that these quantities are responses to impulsive (δ-function like) excitations. The parameter $\alpha_{1,2}$ (decay amplitudes), $\tau_{1,2}$ (fluorescence lifetimes), r_{∞} (limiting anisotropy), ϕ (rotational relaxation time) were determined so that the convoluted products $g(t)^{*} I_{T} \delta (t)$ and $g(t)^{*} I_{T} \delta (t) r^{\delta} (t)$, best fitted the observed $I_{T}(t)$ and $I_{D}(t)$ respectively[17,4]. The fundamental anisotropy was taken to be 0.395 for DPH and TMA-DPH[4,18] and was assumed to be similar for DPH-PC. Calculations were performed on a LSI 11/2 or FACOM 230-75 computer.

The cone angle, θ_{c} was calculated from r_{∞} using the relationship:

$$r_{\infty}/r_{o} = \cos^2 \theta_{c} (1 + \cos \theta_{c})^{2}/4 \qquad ...(4)$$

where θ_{c} is the half angle of a hypothetical cone inside which the fluorophore is assumed to perform a 'wobbling' motion according to the 'wobbling-in-cone' model[4]. The wobbling diffusion constant D_{w} was estimated from the following equation, where $x = \cos \theta_c$ [19], which is equivalent to the original numerical result [20]

$$D_w \phi \; (r_0 - r_\infty)/r_0 = -x^2 \; (1 + x^2) \; (\ln \; ((1 + x)/2) + (1 - x)/2)$$

$$/ \; 2(1 - x) \; + \; (1 - x) \; (6 + 8x - x^2 - 12 \; x^3 - 7x^4) 24 \ldots (5)$$

Results and Discussion

The decays of the total fluorescence intensities of DPH, TMA-DPH and DPH-PC in SR membranes are shown in figure 1. The decay of DPH fluorescence intensity can be described as mono-exponential within reasonable limits. This was, however, not the case for the other probes, and a fitted curve giving two lifetimes was found more adequate. Nevertheless all data, including that for DPH, was routinely analyzed in the form of a double exponential decay (Table 1). The fluorescence properties of various DPH analogues have been previously described [21,22] and biexponential decays of fluorescence intensity of TMA-DPH [18] and DPH-PC reported [15].

The r_∞ or θ_c values derive from the long lived component and if a significant proportion of the probe decays with a short lifetime then the r_∞ value may only reflect the properties of a portion of the probe molecules. Also D_w, as calculated by the approximation of equation 5 (above), may partially reflect a decreasing contribution from the short-lived component. Thus the multiexponential decay property of TMA-DPH and DPH-PC

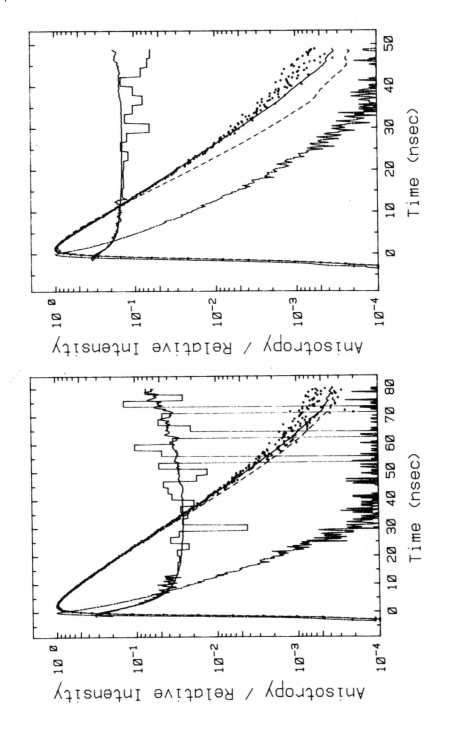

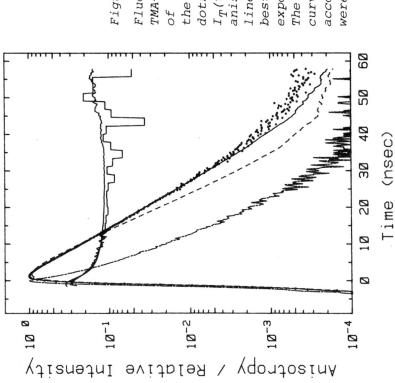

Figure 1

Fluorescence decays of DPH (A), TMA-DPH (B) and DPH-PC (C) in liposomes of SR membrane lipids. Chain line, the instrumental response function, $g(t)$; dots, the totalfluorescence intensity, $I_T(t)$; zigzag solid curves, fluorescence anisotrophy, $r(t)$. The broken and solid lines superimposed on $I_T(t)$ are calculated best-fit curves for single- and double-exponential approximations, respectively. The smooth line superimposed on the $r(t)$ curve is the calculated best-fit curve according to eqn 3. Experimental details were as described in Materials and Methods.

Anisotropy / Relative Intensity

Time (nsec)

detract somewhat from their suitability as probes of lipid motion. However, they have a decided advantage over DPH in having a predictable location in the lipid bilayer[18]. Furthermore the use of the three probes together offer a useful comparison; TMA-DPH probing the C1 - C10 region and being under phospholipid head group influence, DPH-PC probing the central region of the fatty acyl chain and having the same type of motional constraint as a phospholipid sn-2 fatty acyl chain and DPH probing the middle of the bilayer. Furthermore from the size of DPH one would expect some overlap with DPH-PC reflecting motions detected by both TMA-DPH and DPH, notwithstanding long range interactions.

Comparison of the motional parameter of the probes in the presence (SR membrane) and absence (SR membrane lipids) of protein reveal distinct differences between the probes (Table 1). The considerable restriction in probe orientational motion (θ_c), in the case of DPH, by membrane proteins, has been previously documented[8,9]. The extent of restriction, with θ_c decreasing from 71.7 deg. to 56.7 deg. (Table 1) is considerable and the possibility of specific interactions with proteins has been previously suggested[23]. Of course the actual values of the parameters are model dependent and comparisons are made in the relative sense. The order of the decrease of θ_c, by protein, on the probe motion is DPH (15 deg. decrease) > TMA-DPH (7.9 deg) > DPH-PC (5.3 deg), which differs from the order of the actual values of θ_c (with or without protein) which is

Table 1

Fluorescence Parameters of DPH, TMA-DPH and DPH-PC in SR Membranes and Membrane Lipid Liposomes

SR Intact Membranes

	r^s	r_∞	θ_C (deg)	ϕ (ns)	D_W	α_1	τ_1 (ns)	α_2	τ_2 (ns)
DPH	0.123	0.071	56.7	1.33	0.151	0.26	1.54	0.74	8.67
TMA-DPH	0.236	0.182	39.8	0.57	0.209	0.69	1.51	0.31	5.14
DPH-PC	0.192	0.132	46.8	1.26	0.123	0.56	1.53	0.44	7.33

SR Membrane Lipid Liposomes

	r^s	r_∞	θ_C (deg)	ϕ (ns)	D_W	α_1	τ_1 (ns)	α_2	τ_2 (ns)
DPH	0.076	0.017	71.7	1.05	0.236	0.28	2.03	0.72	8.00
TMA-DPH	0.200	0.125	47.7	0.96	0.166	0.73	1.48	0.27	5.16
DPH-PC	0.180	0.097	52.1	1.04	0.174	0.72	1.52	0.28	4.94

r^s, steady state anisotropy; r_∞, residual equilibrium anisotropy; θ_C, cone angle; ϕ, apparent rotational relaxation time; D_W, wobbling diffusion constant; τ_1, τ_2 and α_1, α_2, fluorescence lifetimes and respective decay amplitudes under double exponential approximation and respective decay amplitudes.

DPH > DPH-PC > TMA-DPH. This may be ascribed to the different nature of the probes. Firstly DPH is untethered and would be able to gain access to relatively more inaccessible positions on or between proteins. Some of these sites may deviate considerably from the bilayer normal. The DPH of DPH-PC being tethered to a phosphos-pholipid will not be free to assume many of the otherwise available sites on or between proteins. TMA-DPH is susceptible to interactions with charged species on the protein, however, this would still leave the DPH portion free to perform swinging motions in the hydro-phobic region and it is difficult to see why TMA-DPH should be relatively less constrained in the presence of protein, compared to DPH-PC, unless the locations in the SR membrane were distinct.

Consideration of the rate of motion in terms of D_w shows that although the range of motion (θ_c) is greater for DPH as compared to TMA-DPH, the rate of motion (D_w) is greater for TMA-DPH. Also the order in the presence of protein is TMA-DPH > DPH > DPH-PC, different from the case without protein which is DPH > DPH-PC $\simeq$ TMA-DPH. Again this may be evidence for a difference in the location of the probes, apart from the different positioning longitudinally as mentioned in the Introduction.

Studies of the effects of non-esterified fatty acids on SR membranes are also indicative of a difference in the regions sensed by the different probes. The addition of oleic acid decreased the steady state aniostropy of all three probes[24] but only DPH showed a recovery to the control value. Other studies of the interaction of fatty acids with reconstituted SR ATPase[25,26] also indicate two types of binding site on the protein, an 'annular site' and 'non-annular site', and fatty acids were shown to have a lower affinity for the annular site. It is possible that TMA-DPH and DPH may show differences from DPH-PC and natural membrane phospholipids in the affinity for the different hydrophobic regions available to membrane lipids on the surface of proteins.

Summary and Perspectives

In this work we have shown that the three different DPH probes are useful for examining protein-lipid interactions. In examining the SR membrane the time-resolved fluorescence parameters were found to reflect not only the nature of the probe, but the location in the bilayer. Also some indications of non-random localisation of the probes indicated a heterogeneity in the protein-lipid interfacial regions.

Acknowledgements

This work was supported by the special coordination funds for promoting science and technology and a research grant for

'Solar Energy-Photosynthesis' given by the Agency of Science and Technology of Japan, the SERC (UK) and a Royal Society Study Visit Award (CDS).

References

1. M. Shinitsky, and Y. Barenholz, (1978) *Biochim.Biophys. Acta* **515**,367-394.

2. L.A. Chen, R.E. Dale, S. Roth and L. Brand (1977) *J. Biol.Chem.* **252**, 2163-2169.

3. R.E. Dale, L.A.Chen, and L. Brand (1977) *J. Biol.Chem.* **252**, 7500-7510.

4. S. Kawato, K. Kinosita, Jr., and A. Ikegami (1977) *Biochemistry* **16**, 2319-2324.

5. W.R. Veach, and L. Stryer (1977) *J.Mol.Biol.* **117**, 1109-1113.

6. S. Kawato, K. Kinosita, Jr., and A. Ikegami (1978) *Biochemistry* **17**, 5026-5031.

7. C.D. Stubbs, T. Kouyama, K.Kinosita, Jr., and A, Ikegami (1981) *Biochemistry* **20**, 4257-4262.

8. K. Kinosita Jr., S. Kawato, A. Ikegami, S. Yoshida and Y. Orii (1981) *Biochim.Biophys.Acta.* **647**, 7-17.

9. K.Kinosita, Jr., R. Kataoka, Y.Kimura, O. Gotoh, and A. Ikegami (1981) *Biochemistry* **20**,4270-4277.

10. J. Seelig, L. Tamm, L. Hymel, and S. Fleischer (1981) *Biochemistry* **20**, 3922-3932.

11. W. Hoffman, M.G. Sarzala, and D. Chapman (1979) *Proc. Nat.Acad.Sci.* **76**,3860-3864.

12. F. Jahnig., H. Vogel, and L. Best (1982) *Biochemistry* **21**,6790-6798.

13. M.P. Andrich, and J.M. Vanderkooi (1976) *Biochemistry* **15**,1257-1261.

14. G.B. Warren, P.A. Toon, N.J.M. Birdsall, A.G. Lee, and J.C. Metcalfe (1974) *Proc.Nat.Acad.Sci.*71, 622-626.

15. C.G. Morgan, E.W. Thomas, T.S. Moras, and Y.P. Yianni (1982) *Biochim.Biophys.Acta* **692**,196-201.

16. E.G. Bligh, and W.J. Dyer (1959) *Can.J.Biochem. Physiol.* **37**,911-917.

17. K. Kinosita, Jr., S. Mitaku, A. Ikegami, N.Ohbo, and J.L. Kunii (1976) *Jpn.J.App.Phys.* **15**,2433-2440.

18. L.W. Engel, and F.G. Prendergast (1981) *Biochemistry* **20**,7338-7345.

19. G. Lipari and A. Szabo (1980) *Biophys.J.* **30**,489-506.

20. K. Kinosita, Jr., S. Kawato and A.Ikegami (1977) *Biophys.J.* **20**,289-305.

21. R.B. Cundall, I.D. Johnson, M.W. Jones, E.W. Thomas and I.H. Munro (1979) *Chem.Phys.Lett.***64**,39-42.

22. R.H. Bisby, R.B. Cundall, L. Davenport, I.D. Johnson and E.W. Thomas (1981) *Fluorescent Probes* (G.S. Beddard and M.A. West, eds.) pp97-111, Acad.Press.

23. M.G. Rockley and D.S. Najjar (1981) *Biochim. Biophys.Acta.* **644**,96-100.

24. C.D. Stubbs, K.Kinosita Jr., F. Munkonge, P.J.Quinn and A. Ikegami (1983) Unpublished.

25. B. Mely-Goubert and M.H. Freedman (1980) *Biochim. Biophys.Acta.* **601**, 315-327.

26. A.G. Lee, J.M. East, O.T. Jones, J. McWhirter, E.K. Rooney and A.C. Simmonds (1982) *Biochemistry* 21 6441-6446.

Picosecond Kinetics of Excited State Relaxation in a Tetrapyrrole Pigment[†]

Alfred R. Holzwarth, Joachim Wendler, Kurt Schaffner
Max-Planck-Institut für Strahlenchemie, D-4330 Mülheim a.d. Ruhr, West Germany

Villy Sundström, Åke Sandström and Tomas Gillbro
Division of Physical Chemistry, University of Umeå, S-90187, Sweden

Abstract

The relaxation processes of biliverdin IXα dimethyl ester have been studied by time-resolved absorption and fluorescence detection, using pump-probe and single-photon timing techniques, respectively. The results complement and extend those of earlier investigations[3-6]. In various solvents up to four emitting species, two short-lived (picosecond) and two long-lived ones (nanosecond), have been detected. We conclude that the radiationless relaxation of the short-lived excited states is simultaneously induced by both proton transfer processes and conformational changes, as previously proposed already[4]. The spectroscopic properties of the long-lived species point to the presence of relatively rigid conformations of the bilatriene in liquid solutions at room temperature.

[†] A full account of this work is in press[1]

Introduction*

Open-chain tetrapyrroles are highly flexible chromophores; they are found, inter alia, in photobiologically important biliproteins. In view of their biological relevance and their structural features, which are of quite general interest, the photochemistry and photophysics of these compounds have been actively studied recently[2]. As an example, the tetrapyrrole BVE has roused interest as a model chromophore for the photochromic plant chromoprotein phytochrome and the light-harvesting pigments of cyanobacteria and red algae[3-13].

Our own investigations[3-6] into BVE were concerned, in part with the characterization of the conformational heterogeneity in solution as a function of solvent nature, temperature, and pH[4-6]. Fluorescence quantum yield determinations and laser-induced optoacoustic spectroscopy also led to results regarding possible decay modes of the excited state which are quite complex and not yet fully understood[4,6]. The complexity should not be too surprising, however, in view of the large number of possible configurational, conformational and tautomeric forms which these molecules may adopt. The study of

* *Abbreviations*: BVE, Biliverdin dimethyl ester; MTHF, 2-methyl-tetrahydrofuran; ns, nanosecond; PP, pump-probe; ps, picosecond; RT, room temperature; SPT, single-photon timing.

detailed aspects of radiationless relaxation has been particularly impaired by considerable overlaps of the absorption and fluorescence spectra of the different BVE forms in any given solution.

Biliverdin IXα dimethyl ester (BVE)

Time-resolved studies of the excited state relaxation of BVE in various solvents were to overcome some of the above obstacles, and to elucidate the relations between structure and radiationless processes of individual species. The final goal of any such investigation will be the understanding of the factors determining selective relaxation, i.e the routing of the excitation energy into radiative, radiationless, and photochemical channels. The fast relaxation kinetics of BVE required the use of ps techniques. The combination of transient absorption and fluorescence lifetime spectroscopy is superior to the application of just any one of these methods. A surprising result of these measurements is the occurrence of components with relatively long, ns lifetimes in liquid solution.

Experimental

For the purification of BVE and the solvents see reference 1. Some triethylamine was added to all solutions in order to avoid any protonation of BVE[4].

Transient Absorption Techniques

Ps absorption recovery was measured by the PP technique[14-15]. The ps pulse source was a synchronously pumped, mode-locked and cavity-dumped dye laser (Spectra-Physics) producing pulses of 2 - 8 ps (full-width half maximum, depending on operation conditions) at a repetition rate of 82 kHz[16]. The pulse widths were determined by background-free second harmonic generation in a 1 mm thick KDP crystal. An average laser power of $\sim$ 0.5 mW was used for excitation. Rhodamines 6G and B served to cover the wavelength range of 584 - 660 nm in the dye laser. The concentration of BVE was adjusted to give an absorbance of 0.4 - 0.9 in a 1 mm cell (corresponding to $\sim$ 3 - 7 x 10^{-4} M) at the pump wavelength.

Most experiments were carried out with an early version of the ps spectrometer having a delay line with a time range of only $\sim$ 160 ps. Some others have been performed more recently with an instrument using a modified optical set-up allowing for delay times > 1 ns.

The analysis beam was polarized at the magic angle (54.7°) relative to the excitation beam in order to

obtain rotation-free lifetimes. The lifetimes of ground
state recovery were calculated by computer fitting of the
kinetic data to a sum of exponential decays.

The experiments were normally carried out in a 1 mm
cell with a stationary sample solution. Measurements
with the EtOH solution at RT which were performed in a
flow cell using a peristaltic pump, gave identical
results, indicating that the kinetics observed were not
affted by the accumulation of long-lived photoproducts. In
the low-temperature experiments an Oxford Instruments DN 704
cryostat maintained the temperature constant within $\pm$ 1°C.

In order to overcome the poor solubility in EtOH, BVE and
the solvent were refluxed for ca. 20 min. The heating
simultaneously provided for a better reproducible composition
of BVE forms in the solution, generally with somewhat more
of the long-lived component(s) present in a given solvent
(see below for a similar effect of sonication, and the
Discussion) [17].

Fluorescence Lifetime Measurements
The fluorescence lifetimes were measured by the SPT technique.
The same laser type as above was used with rhodamine 6G as
the dye[18]. The fluorescence was selected by a double
monochromator with a 4 nm bandwidth. A red-sensitive photomultiplier with a multi-alkali photocathode in a cooled
housing was used for detection. The width of the apparatus

function, as measured from a dilute Ludox scatterer, was $\sim$ 200 ps (full-width half maximum). The SPT resolution was checked by measuring the fluorescence lifetimes of crypto-cyanine in MeOH (42 ps) and EtOH (76 ps), and of 1, 1'-diethyl-2, 2'-dicarbocyanine iodide in EtOH (15 ps) at RT. The agreement with published data is excellent, e.g., 48 ps and 75 ps for cryptocyanine in MeOH and EtOH, respectively[19]. For the diethyldicarbocyanine iodide in EtOH a re-examination by the PP technique gave a lifetime of 23 ± 2 ps. These data indicate that we can presently measure lifetimes down to ca. 20 ps.

The fluorescence decay was again observed through a polarizer set at the magic angle. The decay times were analysed in terms of a sum-of-exponentials decay law using a semi-linear Marquardt algorithm in an iterative convolution method[20].

The concentration of BVE in all fluorescence measurements was 1 x 10^{-5} M. The solutions were sonicated for $\sim$ 30 min in a Sonorex AK 255 ultrasonicator bath (35 kHz, 250 W) in order to obtain a reproducible composition of BVE forms in the solution (see above for a similar effect of heating and the Discussion)[17]. The composition reached after sonication did not change upon standing of the solutions. All measurements were carried out at 22 ± 2°C.

Results

Ground State Recovery Kinetics of BVE

The ground state recovery times of BVE in several solvents at RT are summarized in Table 1. The PP measurements were carried out, whenever possible, at two different PP wavelengths λ_d. Bleaching signals were observed in all cases. The lifetimes of the components of the biexponential decays in EtOH and EtOD varied somewhat with λ_d. With regard to the error limits of our instrumentation, these differences are insufficient to warrant interpretation at this time. Their relative intensities, however, depended much more clearly on λ_d. The signals of BVE were quite generally at least one order of magnitude smaller than those of other compounds, e.g., cyanine dyes, with comparable lifetimes and under similar conditions[16]. This reduced signal strength is possibly attributable to a strong $^1S \rightarrow {}^nS$ excited state absorption. The occurrence of any decay components in the ns range could not be excluded in these experiments because of the limited time range of the optical delay line ($\sim$ 160 ps) used.

Two decays in the ps range were observed at RT in EtOH (Table 1). Low signal intensity and high scattering, caused by precipitation of BVE in the relatively concentrated solutions upon cooling prevented a study of the temperature dependence of these lifetimes in EtOH below RT. However, such a study was possible in EtOD, in which BVE is somewhat more soluble. At the same time, a

Table 1

Lifetimes of Excited-state BVE Measured by the Pump-Probe Technique

Solvent	Excitation-Detection Wavelength	Lifetimes*			Relative Amplitude
	λ_d, nm	τ_1' ps	τ_2' ps	τ_3' ps	$A(\tau_1)/A(\tau_2)$
EtOH	605	19	73	–	1.7
EtOD	605	17	57	–	1.5
EtOH ·	643	12	68	–	3
EtOD	643	15	$\sim$55	–	>5
MeOH	640	–	51#	1200†	1.3[+]
MTHF	640	20	64	–	$\sim$0.5

* Maximum errors in lifetimes are ± 10% for double-exponential analyses and ± 5% for single exponentials.

\# This lifetime possibly represents an average value of two components; triple-exponential analysis was not possible, however, given the signal/noise ratio and the large amplitude of the long-lived decay.

† Since our apparatus is not suited for precise measurements of decays > 1 ns, this value may only be a lower limit to the actual lifetime. It may therefore be taken to simply indicate the presence of a nanosecond component.

+ $A(\tau_2)/A(\tau_3)$.

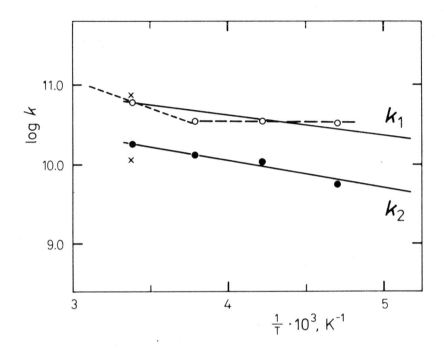

Figure 1

*Temperature dependence of the ps decay rate
constants k_1 and k_2 of the BVE transients τ_1 and τ_2,
respectively, in EtOD, as determined by the PP
technique; λ_d = 643 nm. Open circles: fast
compnents; full circles: slow components; crosses:
RT data in EtOH. The short dashes denominate the
temperature-(viscosity-) dependent part of the
decay of τ_1, and the longer dashes denominate the
temperature-independent proton transfer process of
the τ_1 component (see Discussion).*

possible deuterium isotope effect on the radiationless decay of BVE[4] could also be explored. The results are shown in figure 1. Two decays were observed, with activation energies of 408 cm^{-1} (short-lived component; all data points considered) and 520 cm^{-1} (long-lived component) (Table 2). These values should be compared with the activation energy of ca.1000 cm^{1} of the solvent viscosity.

The measurements in solvents other than EtOH and EtO^{2}H were carried out using the set-up with the long delay line. All data are compiled in Table 1.

Table 2

Activation Energies of Ground State Repopulation Kinetics of
BVE from the Data of figure 1; λ_d = 643 nm; in EtOD

Activation Energy	Comment
E_A, cm^{-1}	
408	short-lived picosecond component τ_1; full line for k_1 in figure 1 (all data points included)
520	long-lived picosecond component τ_2
$\overset{>}{-}$ 920	short dashes for k_1 line in figure 1

Fluorescence Measurements

The stationary fluorescence spectra, measured at two different λexc's (580 and 640 nm) each, are reproduced in reference 1. The spectrum in EtOH is virtually identical with that shown already in an earlier paper[5]. The spectra differ in the ratios of red (∿ 650 nm) to far-red (∿ 710 -720 nm) fluorescence intensity. MeOH on the one hand and MTHF on the other hand are on the extremes, with the latter exhibiting the highest proportion of far-red emission.

In every solvent the red/far-red intensity ratio depends on the way how the solution had been prepared. In general, the red fluorescence increases with the extent of sonication and warming of the solution, until a limit is reached which depends on the particular solvent (cf. experimental part). For this reason, all fluorescence data refer to solutions which had been sonicated prior to measurement, unless stated otherwise.

In most solvents the decays obtained required up to four exponential functions in the fit (figures 2-4 and Table 3).

An analysis of fluorescence decays in terms of three or even four exponentials, as has been necessary here in some cases, is highly demanding on the quality of the experimental data. Analyses of SPT data have been carried out previously with good success in terms of three[18,21]

and four exponentials[22]. Considering the statistics of the
problem, an analysis of a decay curve in terms of even four
exponentials requires certain conditions be fulfilled.
Most important is that

a)   the laser and detection systems are extremely
     stable during the time of the measurement,

b)   the lifetimes are well separated,

c)   the shortest-lived component has a large relative
     amplitude.

Conditions (a) and (b) are clearly met by our instrumentation
and the data obtained (Table 3), respectively, and condition
(c) is fulfilled in all solvents except MeOH. Weighted
residual plots are prerequisite for the judging of the fits
and the decision with regard to the appropriate kinetic
model. This is clearly illustrated by our data as shown,
e.g., in figures 2 and 3. The Chi^2 test alone is insufficient
and inconclusive in cases of several components.

The validity of the analyses in terms of three and four
exponential decays was tested by convoluting the calculated
decays with the experimental excitation function. Computer-
generated Poissonian noise was then added to the convoluted
decay[23]. The parameters could be extracted again from these
simulated decays, within the given error limits, by our
fitting program. The distinction between three and four
exponentials was thus clearly possible under our
conditions.

Table 3
Lifetimes, Relative Yields, and Relative Amplitudes of the Fluorescence Decay Components of BVE Measured by the Single-Photon Timing Technique

Solvent	λ^{exc}, nm	λ^{em}, nm	Lifetimes, ps*				Normalized Relative Amplitudes, %†				Normalized Relative Yields, %			
			τ_1	τ_2	τ_3	τ_4	A_1	A_2	A_3	A_4	ϕ_1	ϕ_2	ϕ_3	ϕ_4
MTHF	580	650	26	112	1377	4225	85	14	0.5	0.5	34	23	11	32
"	"	710	22	89	1896	–	84	16	<1	–	54	42	4	–
"	640	660	–	93	1695	4545	–	84	4	12	–	12	9	79
"	"	710	–	78	968	4183	–	98	1.2	0.8	–	62	10	28
MeOH	580	650	–	140	–	4678	–	44	–	56	–	2	–	98
"	"	710	–	52	–	4589	–	85	–	15	–	6	–	94
"	640	660	–	–	–	4612	–	–	–	100	–	–	–	100
"	"	710	38	–	630	4592	89	–	2	9	8	–	3	89

EtOH	580	650	19	249	1639	4601	92	5	1	2	15	11	16	58
"	"	710	10	112	910	3997	98	2	<0.2	<0.1	57	9	8	26
"	640	660	--	97	879	4610	--	69	21	10	--	4	27	69
"	"	710	--	56	710	4043	--	94	5	1	--	40	25	35

* The τ values correspond to the T values given in the insets of figures 2-4. The ordering $\tau_1...\tau_n$ (increasing lifetimes) does not correspond to the ordering $T_1...T_n$. Errors in lifetime are ± 10% or ± 5 ps, whichever is larger, except for single-exponential analyses in which the error is ± 1%. For components with a relative amplitude of less than 1% the errors in lifetime may be up to ± 20%.

+ The amplitudes $A_1...A_n$ are normalized to 100%, unlike the corresponding values $B_1...B_n$ given in the insets of figures 2-4. The errors in amplitude are also ca. ± 10% for three- and four-exponential analyses.

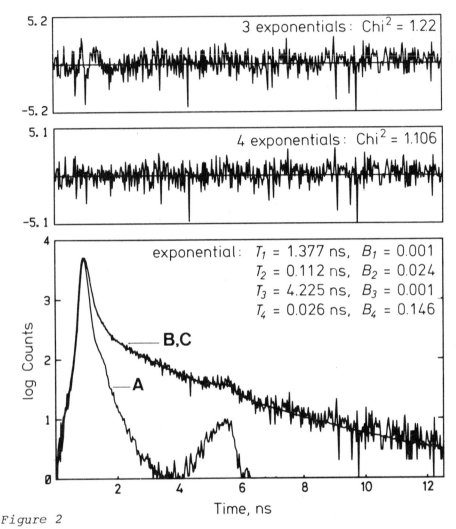

Figure 2

Semilogarithmic plot of fluorescence decay of BVE in MTHF at RT; λ^{exc} = 580 nm, λ^{em} = 650 nm. **Note:** *The semilogarithmic plots of the exciting pulse (A), the measured decay (B), and the decay function calculated from the best-fit kinetic parameters (C) are shown. In the inset the calculated lifetimes $T_1 \ldots T_n$ and amplitudes $B_1 \ldots B_n$ of the decay components are given. Immediately above, a weighted residuals plot indicates the deviations of these computer-fitted parameters from the measured decay, with the Chi^2 value in the inset. On top a similar plot for an n - 1 component analysis is added for the purpose of comparison.*

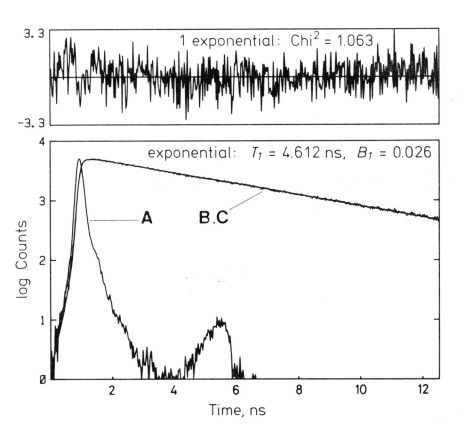

Figure 3

Semilogarithmic plot of fluorescence decay of BVE in MTHF at RT; $\lambda^{exc} = 580$ nm, $\lambda^{em} = 710$ nm. See also the Note of figure 2.

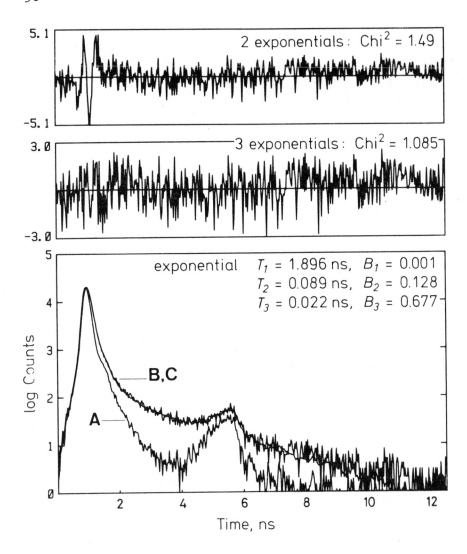

Figure 4

Semilogarithmic plot of fluorescence decay of BVE in MeOH at RT; $\lambda^{exc} = 640$ nm, $\lambda^{em} = 660$ nm. See also the Note of figure 2.

Discussion

Our data shows that the relaxation kinetics of BVE are quite complex. In general, a greater number of decay components could be found by the SPT technique than by transient absorption spectroscopy. This is due to the fact that the SPT technique covers a considerably larger dynamic range (> 3 orders of magnitude) than the PP technique (ca. 1-2 orders of magnitude). Thus, the ns components are observed by PP only when their relative amplitude is large as, e.g., in MeOH.

When the results obtained by the two techniques are compared, the excellent agreement for the shortest-lived decay component τ_1 (ps) becomes evident. For τ_2 (ps), most values from the two techniques agree also reasonably well, pointing to a decay component with $\tau \sim 60 - 90$ ps. Any difference between the often slightly longer fluorescence lifetimes and the PP data generally appears negligible. Only in the case with $\lambda^{exc} = 580$ nm and $\lambda^{em} = 650$ nm the τ_2 values in fluorescence are significantly larger in all solvents examined (cf. Table 3), both in relation to the PP measurements and to fluorescence data at other λ^{exc}'s and λ^{em}'s. In any given solvent, the τ_3 (ns) component shows the largest nonsystematic variations in fluorescence, while the τ_4 (ns) values are reasonably constant.

The Nanosecond Components (τ_3 and τ_4)

In all solvents λ^{exc} and λ^{em} of the ns components coincide very well with the data of the previously identified red-emitting form(s)[5]. An ns lifetime is unexpectedly long for this BVE chromophore which, by reference to theoretical calculations[24-27], has been assigned a stretched conformation[5]. The relatively narrow excitation and emission spectra, the resolved vibrational structure, the small Stokes shifts, and the long lifetimes indicate now that these chromophores should possess a relatively rigid and uniform conformation and a high fluorescence quantum yield. Inasmuch as the analogy between the phycobiliprotein chromophores and BVE is valid, our results suggest that, in contrast to the generally accepted previous view, tetrapyrroles can adopt *inherently* rigid conformations. However, a full characterization of the molecular form of these conformations with long fluorescence lifetimes is still lacking.

The Picosecond Components (τ_1 and τ_2)

The ps components can be identified with the previously described far-red emitting species of BVE[5], with $\lambda^{em}_{max} \sim$ 710 nm.

The data clearly require two different excited-state species to account for the two fast decays. The broad structureless spectra, the relatively large Stokes shifts,

and the short lifetimes point to a highly flexible nature
of these emitters. This does not necessarily imply,
however, that there exist two corresponding different
ground state species. A bi-exponential decay of excited
BVE in the ps range has been observed in EtOH, EtOD and
MTHF by the PP technique. The relative intensities of the
two components depend on the excitation/detection wavelengths and the temperature (determined only in EtOD)
(see Table 1 and figure 1). This suggests that there are
two different excited-state species responsible for the
biexponential decay. The results fully agree with the
finding of the two ps components τ_1 and τ_2 by the SPT
measurements in all solvents except MeOH.

When a straight line is drawn through all data points
which describe the temperature dependence of the short-
lived component in EtOD (figure 1: solid line), an
activation energy of 408 cm^{-1} is obtained. However,
there is ample evidence against a linear dependence of
log k vs. $1/T$. Firstly, the fit with the measured data
is poor. Secondly, a linear dependence should result in
a much larger temperature dependence of the fluorescence
quantum yields than has been observed experimentally[4].
And finally, the hypothetical lifetime at 77K calculated
from this slope is greater by more than one order of
magnitude when compared to the one derived from the
quantum yield[4]. In contrast to the relaxation data of

the long-lived component, those of the short-lived component are independent of temperature below $\sim$ 260K in EtOD Consequently, the log k vs. $1/T$ function of this latter species can be resolved, in good agreement with the data, into a sum of a temperature-dependent and a temperature-independent relaxation process according to eq (1). On this basis a lower limit to the

$$k_{nr} = k_{nr}^{(0)} + k_{nr}^{(1)} \times \exp\left(-\frac{E_A}{K_B T}\right) \quad \ldots \ (1)$$

activation energy E_A of $\sim$ 920 cm^{-1} (= 12 kJ/mol) is estimated from figure 1 (short dashes). Such a dependence is readily rationalized in terms of a fast and temperature-independent intramolecular proton transfer, which is most likely to occur between the nitrogens of rings B and C. This transfer induces radiationless deactivation at a rate of 3.5 x 10^{10} s^{-1}, and it parallels a temperature- (or rather viscosity-) dependent relaxation mechanism which can be correlated with twisting around the methine-ring bonds. The activation energy for this twisting is now in the range of the solvent activation energy, which indicates that the solvent viscosity contributes more to the activation energy than do intramolecular barriers. This resembles, inter alia, the situation for the cyanine dyes[19] which have been used as calibration substances in this work.

In order to further support our interpretation, it would have been desirable to obtain PP data at higher than RT.

Unfortunately, however, the fastest component was too
short for a reliable determination under such conditions.

The temperature dependence of the longer-lived (τ_2)
of the ps components can be well fitted by a straight
line. Fast proton transfer between the central nitrogens
does not seem to contribute to relaxation in this species.
The slower decay might arise from other tautomers, i.e.
lactims, or from conformational isomers. The activation
energy of 520 cm^{-1} ($\sim$ 6 kJ/mol) points to a predominant
role of intramolecular barriers for this relaxation
process. This is possibly in contrast to the situation
of the shorter-lived component τ_1. In MeOH solution only
the longer-lived component τ_2 is detected. The absence
of the shorter-lived species τ_1 suggests that the solvent
properties are important for the occurrence of the proton
transfer process.

Our results do not allow a straightforward answer to
the question of whether the ps decays are due to one,
two or even more ground state species. However, this
may in fact not even be a reasonable question to ask,
since the potential energy minima are expected to be
quite flat, and they are possibly separated by activation
barriers which are small in comparison to the thermal
energy.

There remains to mention that single-shot ps

measurements of etiobiliverdin with transient absorption and
fluorescence detection have been reported[28]. No ns component
has been found in this study, and the data for the ps
relaxation range differed with the two methods employed, in
contrast to our own results with BVE.

Conclusion

The relaxation processes of BVE were investigated by a
combination of PP and SPT techniques. The results supplement
data obtained previously with stationary methods (absorption,
fluorescence, solvent-induced CD)[4,5] and with methods of
limited time resolution (optoacoustic spectroscopy)[3], on the
basis of which the heterogeneities in the spectral behaviour
have been proposed to arise from different ground-state
conformers in solution. It now appears, in fact, that the
situation is even more complex. Up to four fluorescing
species have been detected which can be attributed to either
three or four ground state species. While the radiationless
relaxation of the short-lived (ps) excited states appears to
be induced by proton transfer and conformational changes, it
is of a more general photobiological interest to note that
the longer-lived (ns) species derive their stability from
the rigidity of their conformation (ground and excited
states). In other words, BVE can adopt relatively rigid
conformations even at RT in solution, i.e., without external
stabilization effected by intermolecular interactions (e.g.,
in phycobiliproteins). Intramolecular stabilizing forces
evidently suffice.

Acknowledgements

ARH thanks the University of Umeå and the Swedish Natural Science Research Council for travel grants to Umeå. The work at the MPI für Strahlenchemie was assisted by Mrs G. Wojciechowski (preparation of BVE), Miss A. Keil and Mr H.-V. Seeling (emission spectroscopy), and Mr W Schuster (data handling).

References

1. A.R. Holzwarth, J. Wendler, K. Schaffner, V. Sundström,
   A. Sandström and T. Gillbro, *Isr. J. Chem.*, in press
   (1983).

2. Review: H. Scheer, *Angew. Chem.*, **93**, 230 (1981); *Angew.
   Chem.Int.Ed.*, **20**, 241 (1981).

3. S.E.Braslavsky, R.M. Ellul, R.G. Weiss, H. Al-Ekabi and
   K. Schaffner, *Tetrahedron,* in press (1982).

4. A. R. Holzwarth, H. Lehner, S.E. Braslavsky, and K.
   Schaffner, *Liebigs Ann. Chem.,* **2002** (1978).

5. S.E. Braslavsky, A.R. Holzwarth, E.Langer, H. Lehner,
   J.I. Matthews and K. Schaffner, *Isr. J. Chem.,* **20**,
   196 (1980).

6. I.-M. Tegmo-Larsson, S.E. Braslavsky, S. Culshaw, R.M.
   Ellul, C. Nicolau and K. Schaffner, *J. Am. Chem.
   Soc.,* **103**, 7152 (1981).

7. M.J. Burke, D.C. Pratt and A. Moscowitz, *Biochemistry*,
   11, 4025 (1972).

8. P.-S. Song, Q. Chae, D.A. Lightner, W.R. Briggs and
   D. Hopkins, *J.Am.Chem.Soc.,* **95**, 7892 (1973).

9. G. Blauer and G. Wagnière, *J. Am.Chem.Soc.,* 97, 1949
   (1975).

10. R.Gautron, P. Jardon, C. Pétrier, M. Choussy, M. Barbier
    and M. Vuillaume, *Experientia,* **32**, 1100 (1976).

11. H. Scheer and W. Kufer, *Z. Naturforsch.,* **32C**, 513 (1977).

12. H. Falk, K. Grubmayr, E. Haslinger, T. Schlederer and K.
    Thirring, *Monatsh. Chem.,* **109**, 1451 (1978).

13. C. Pétrier, C. Dupuy, P. Jardon and R. Gautron,
    Photochem. Photobiol., **29**, 389 (1979).

14. E.P. Ippen and C.V. Shank, *Top.Appl.Phys.,* **18**, 83 (1977).

15. A.R. Holzwarth, *Laser Optoelektr.*, **14**, 19 (1982).

16. V. Sundström and T. Gillbro,*Appl.Phys.*, **24**,233 (1981).

17. H. Al-Ekabi, I.-M. Tegmo-Larsson, S.E. Braslavsky and K. Schaffner, unpublished results.

18. A.R. Holzwarth, J. Wendler and W.Wehrmeyer, *Photochem Photobiol.*, **36**, 479 (1982).

19. V. Sundström and T. Gillbro, *Chem. Phys.*,**61**,257 (1981).

20. A.E.W. Knight and B.K. Selinger, *Austr. J. Chem.*, **26**, 1 (1973).

21. W. Haehnel, A.R. Holzwarth and J. Wendler, *Photochem. Photo-biol.*, in press.

22. A. Gafni, R.P. Detoma, R.E. Manrow and L. Brand, *Biophys. J.* **17**, 155 (1977).

23. **L.J. Cline Love and L. A. Shaver**, *Anal.Chem.*,**52**, 154 (1980).

24. M.J. Burke, D.C. Pratt and A. Moscowitz, *Biochemistry,* **11**, 4025 (1972).

25. Q. Chae and P.-S. Song, *J.Am.Chem.Soc.*, **97**,4176 (1975).

26. T. Sugimoto, K. Ishikawa and H. Suzuki, *J.Phys. Soc.Jpn.*, **40**, 258 (1976).

27. G. Wagnière and G. Blauer, *J.Am.Chem.Soc.*, **98**, 7806 (1976).

28. M.E.Lippitsch, A.Leitner, M.Riegler and F.R. Aussenegg, *Springer's Series in Chemical Physics,* 14, 327 (1980); idem, *ibid.,* **23**, 323 (1982); idem, *7th Vavilov Conference on Nonlinear Optics,* Akademgorodok/Novosibirsk, 1981.

Picosecond Pulse Amplification and Continuum Generation

A.I. Ferguson

Clarendon Laboratory, Parks Road, Oxford OX1 3PU

Present address
Department of Physics, University of Southampton

Introduction

Dye lasers have proved to be a very reliable source of
ultrashort light pulses throughout the visible region of the
spectrum. In particular, continuously pumped dye lasers,
which are either passively mode-locked or synchronously
pumped, can produce pulses which are subpicosecond in
duration and bandwidth limited. These pulses have somewhat
restricted energy, producing only a few nJ per pulse. In
many applications much higher energy is required. Examples
where this is so is in bleaching studies or where a high
density of excited states is needed such as in studies of
electron-hole plasmas in solids. Furthermore, it is often
necessary to shift the wavelength of the laser pulses to
regions of the spectrum where lasers do not operate. By
using high peak power laser pulses, nonlinear optical
processes such as second harmonic generation or stimulated
Raman scattering can be used to produce short pulses in new
spectral regions.

A popular approach to the generation of more energetic
ultrashort pulses is to start off with a low energy source

from a well behaved dye laser and to amplify these pulses using dye amplifiers[1-4]. Gains of the order of 10^6 are typical, leading to pulse energies in the region of 1 mJ delivered in a picosecond or subpicosecond packet.

I shall describe some amplifier systems suitable for generating energetic ultrashort pulses. A major application for these pulses is in the study of transient absorption. In these applications it is necessary to create a picosecond 'flashlamp'. This 'flashlamp' can be created by focussing very intense light pulses into suitable media. Nonlinear processes generate a picosecond continuum which spans a wavelength region from the ultraviolet to the infrared.

Picosecond pulse amplification

Most picosecond pulse amplifiers which have been described in the literature are straightforward extensions of amplifier systems designed for amplifying cw beams or nanosecond pulses[5,6]. They consist of dye cells, usually flowing, which are either longitudinally or transversely pumped by a powerful laser of several nanoseconds duration. An ideal pump laser for Rh6G dye is a frequency doubled Q-switched Nd:YAG laser at 532nm. Several hundred millijoules of energy are available and this wavelength matches the absorption of Rh6G. The energy is delivered in a time comparable with the fluorescence lifetime of

the dye and so a large inversion can be obtained. When
nanosecond pulses are being amplified conversion efficiencies
of tens of per cent can be achieved[5,6]. However, with picosecond pulses 1% conversion is more typical. The reason for
this is the presence of amplified spontaneous emission (ASE).
When a dye cell is pumped by an intense laser, the single
pass gain can be so great that noise at one end of the cell
is amplified to an extent that the amplified noise saturates
the amplifier at the other end of the cell. For a given
amplifier the gain is therefore drastically reduced. Pumping
this amplifier much harder only ensures that the amplified
spontaneous emission is increased but does little for the
gain experienced by a short pulse passing through the
amplifier[2,7]. As a consequence multiple stage amplifiers
are usually necessary. Analytic solutions for the saturation
of dye amplifiers by amplified spontaneous emission have
been found by Migus *et al*[2]. They are able to calculate the
population inversion in the steady state at any point along
the dye amplifier and hence the small signal single pass
gain, G_o. They find that $G_o = \exp(Z)$

where $Z = (\sigma_{em} + \sigma_{abs}) N_{st} - \sigma_{abs} NL$

The parameter Z is a measure of the stored energy and σ_{em},
σ_{abs} are the emission and absorption cross-sections of the
dye at the input signal wavelength. The parameters N_{st}, N
and L are the stored number density of excited states, the
total number density of dye molecules and the cell length,
respectively.

The single pass gain for a short pulse of arbitrary energy, E_{sig} is given by a well-known expression[8-10]

$$G = (1/S)\ln(1 + G_o(e^S - 1))$$

where S is a measure of the amplifier saturation and is given by

$$S = E_{sig}(\sigma_{em} + \sigma_{abs})/Ah\nu_{sig}$$

and A, ν_{sig} are the area and frequency of the signal beam.

A plot of the saturated gain as a function of normalised input energy, S for various values of stored energy parameter, Z is given in figure 1a. It should be noted that for the range of parameters chosen a single pass gain of 10^6 is not possible. Furthermore, for large small signal gains the amplifier saturates at very small input energy. For small gain the saturation occurs at much higher input energy.

The efficiency of the dye amplifier may also be deduced from figure 1a. Defining the conversion efficiency as the ratio of output quanta to stored quanta we obtain

$$\varepsilon = \frac{(G - 1)s}{Z}$$

A plot of ε as a function of input energy for various values

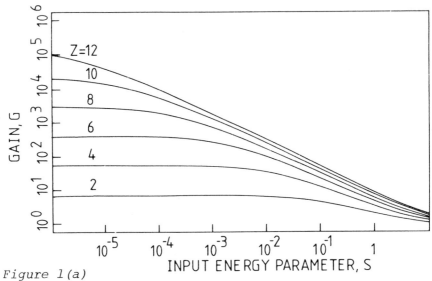

Figure 1(a)
Single pass gain plotted as a function of normalized
input energy parameter S for various values of stored
energy parameter Z, indicated.

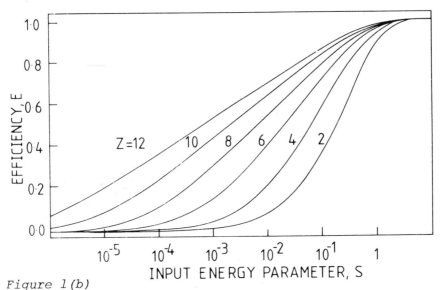

Figure 1(b)
The efficiency of a dye laser amplifier for short
pulses as a function of normalized input energy parameter S
for various values of the stored energy parameter Z.

of stored energy parameter is given in figure 1b. It can be seen that large conversion efficiencies can only be obtained at large input energies when the amplifier is saturated. This can of course be very undesirable as a pulse amplified by a strongly saturated amplifier will be severely distorted and stretched.

When picosecond pulses are to be amplified by a factor of about 10^6 or more it is clear that several stages of amplification will be necessary. In order to keep the number of stages reasonably small the amplifiers are normally operated close to saturation. Figures 1a,b, also show that picosecond amplifiers will not be very efficient.

The analysis outlined above is only applicable where the dye amplifiers are pumped with nanosecond pulses and a quasi-steady state has been reached when the signal pulse arrives. Recent work in which the dye amplifiers are themselves pumped by picosecond pulses has shown that more efficient conversion is possible[11]. However these systems have not yet been shown to produce as much energy as systems pumped with nanosecond pulses and will not be discussed further.

A picosecond pulse amplifier is shown in figure 2 and is typical of many systems which have been developed around the world. This particular system has been designed to amplify pulses from a synchronously pumped rhodamine 6G

114

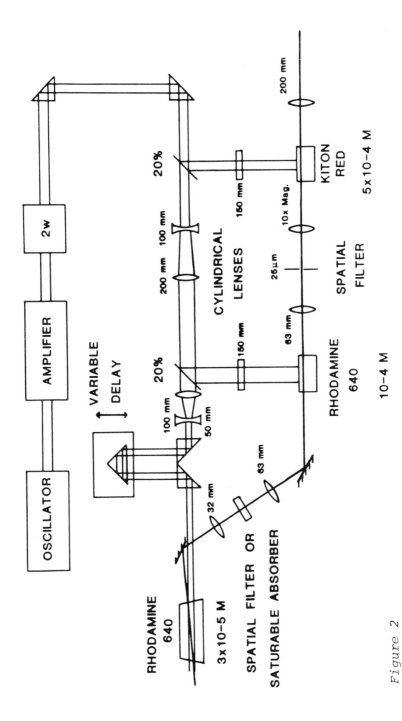

Figure 2

Schematic diagram of an amplifier system capable of amplifying picosecond pulses to the mJ level (after Ferguson and Taylor[4])

dye laser of about 2 psec and tunable around 600nm. The
pump laser is a Q-switched Nd:YAG oscillator and amplifier
(Molectron MY34). The laser output is smoothed by an
intracavity etalon which prevents mode beating. The output
is in the form of a quasi-Gaussian of about 12 nsec
duration with a small amount of high frequency noise.
The output of the laser is frequency doubled and produces
pulses of 140 mJ at 532 nm at a 10 Hz rate. The timing
jitter of the laser is less than 500 psec with respect
to a Q-switch trigger pulse. This enables the synchronisation of Nd:YAG pulse with one of the pulses from the
synchronous train to 500 psec accuracy.

There are three dye cells, two are transversely
pumped and the final stage is longitudinally pumped. The
dyes are chosen to have large absorption at 532 nm but good
emission cross-section at 600 nm. The dye concentration
is adjusted so that the penetration of the pump beam
matches the dimensions of the amplified pulse. This
dimension is determined by the condition that energy
density of the amplified beam be sufficiently large to
obtain good efficiency, as determined by the analysis
represented in figure 1a,b. In the first stage the
input pulse energy is low and the transverse dimension is
small. A high concentration of dye is therefore required.
This implies that a dye of minimum absorption at the
amplified wavelength should be chosen for the first stage
even at the expense of emission cross-section. In the
subsequent stages a smaller concentration of dye is used

and dyes with larger emission and absorption cross-sections at the amplified wavelength may be chosen. By using different dyes in the various amplifier stages the problem of ASE from one dye cell saturating the next cell can be reduced.

The first cell is filled with a flowing solution of Kiton Red at a concentration of 5×10^{-4} M in a 2 per cent solution of Ammonyx LO in water. The length of the cell is 10mm and the pump and amplified beam are focussed to spot size of about 150 µm. The gain of this stage is approximately 10^3 and can be adjusted by varying the percentage coupling of the pump beam onto the dye cell. A spatial filter consisting of a 25 µm pinhole and microscope objective is used to reduce the ASE to less than 1 part in 10^2 of the amplified beam.

The second stage dye is Rhodamine 640 at a concentration of 10^{-4} in a 2 per cent solution of ammonix LO in water. This cell is 20 mm in length and the spot size is approximately 500 µm. The gain in this stage is about 100 and the ASE is kept to a minimum by careful alignment of the pump beam. The resultant ratio of amplified light to ASE is better than 500:1 at this stage.

The third stage is again Rhodamine 640 but at a concentration of 2×10^{-5} M. In this case the cell is longitudinally pumped over its length of 10 cm. The spot size is 2 mm. A variable delay enables the amplification to be optimised. The nett gain for this system is 3×10^6

corresponding to an output pulse energy of 4 mJ. In order to maintain the best pulses from the amplifier, saturable absorbers should be used between stages. These can be in the form of glass filters (Schott RG630) or flowing jets of malachite green dye. In the system described above the ratio of amplified pulse to ASE is about 20:1 without saturable absorbers. In this case a pulse broadening from about 2 psec at the input to about 4 psec at the output is measured. The addition of saturable absorbers reduces ASE and leads to shorter amplified pulses. This system shows a pulse to pulse energy stability of about 10% once equilibrium is achieved.

Recent progress in the generation of pulses of less than 100 fsec using colliding pulse dye lasers has led to the design of amplifiers for these pulses[12,13]. New problems are introduced in amplifier design. The most important of these is the effect of group velocity dispersion in the dye solution and amplifier optics which causes significant temporal broadening. For example, a 75 fsec pulse at 600 nm will be stretched to approximately 410 fsec on passing through 25 cm of water due to group velocity dispersion.

Fortunately, temporal broadening due to group velocity dispersion can be largely removed using a grating pair[14]. A grating pair introduces a delay which increases linearly with wavelength and which can be adjusted to compensate for the approximately linear frequency chirp due to group velocity dispersion. However, other effects which are bound to be present such as nonlinear frequency generation, wavelength dependent gain, saturable absorption and saturable gain introduce a nonlinear frequency chirp which cannot be easily removed. These must be kept to a minimum. Fork *et al*[13] have demonstrated the amplification of 70 fsec optical pulses by extending the type of system shown in figure 3. They have introduced an additional transverse amplifier before the final stage to permit a more gradual increase in pulse energy while including a saturable absorber between each stage. At the final stage the pulse duration was increased to 400 fsec but could be compressed to 90 fsec using a grating pair after the final stage. The output pulse energy was 180 μJ corresponding to a peak power of 2GW.

There are many applications in photochemistry, biology and physics for such short and intense light pulses. We shall not be able to describe specific experiments in the space available but should like to describe a general technique which can be applied in all of the above disciplines using the picosecond continuum source which is made available by energetic picosecond pulses.

Picosecond Continuum Generation

One of the most remarkable effects in nonlinear optics is the generation of broadband short pulse radiation by focussing an intense picosecond pulse into almost any transparent material. This effect is normally called picosecond continuum generation and, as its name suggests,

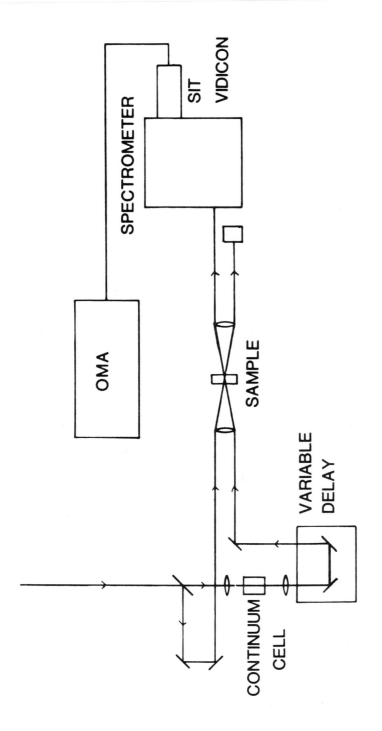

Figure 3

Schematic diagram of a transient absorption experiment using a picosecond continuum generator (after Ferguson and Taylor[4])

provides us with a source of ultrashort pulses from the ultraviolet to the infrared region of the spectrum. The picosecond continuum is synchronous with the exciting pulse and so can be used in time resolved transient absorption measurements.

A schematic diagram of a typical transient absorption experiment is shown in figure 3. An intense picosecond pulse is focussed into a suitable continuum generator and the resulting continuum is passed through the sample. Part of the exciting beam is focussed onto the sample. This beam redistributes the energy in the sample. The recovery of the sample can be observed by monitoring the absorption of the continuum in the sample as a function of wavelength and time. Spectral resolution is provided by a spectrometer and optical multichannel analyser while temporal resolution is provided by varying the path length of the continuum beam. This can provide valuable information about energy transfer within the sample.

Few phenomena in nonlinear optics have been as hotly debated as the reason for picosecond continuum generation. We do not intend to get embroiled in the arguments[15-19]. The facts are quite simple. When an energetic picosecond pulse is focussed to produce peak power densities of about 10^{11} W cm^{-2} and greater in most media, a broad continuum is generated. There appears to be some kind of a threshold for this phenomenon in that below a certain level the emitted spectrum is quite structured. Increasing the power density flattens the spectrum. Further increases in the pump intensity stabilizes the output but has little other effect. The emitted spectrum is well collimated but has a divergence approximately twice that of the pump laser. To a good approximation it is synchronous with the pump beam, although, as we shall see in the femtosecond regime, this is not strictly true.

Some of the explanations for continuum generation include parametric four wave mixing, self-phase modulation, self-focussing and dielectric breakdown[15-19]. The collimation of the continuum suggests some degree of phase-matching and therefore gives some support to the idea that para-metric processes are responsible. However, the kinds of intensities involved are very close to fila-mentary breakdown. There is evidence to suggest that free electrons are generated, thus giving rise to a rapid change in refractive index and causing a frequency chirp due to self-phase modulation. It is likely that some combination of these processes takes place.

There are several factors which go to make a good continuum generator. First, the medium should be transparent at the pump wavelength, preferably with absorptions well outside the visible region. This means that the material is relatively nondispersive and any phase-mismatch in a parametric process will be small. The material should have a high stimulated Raman threshold. If there is a strong Raman line then most of the pump energy

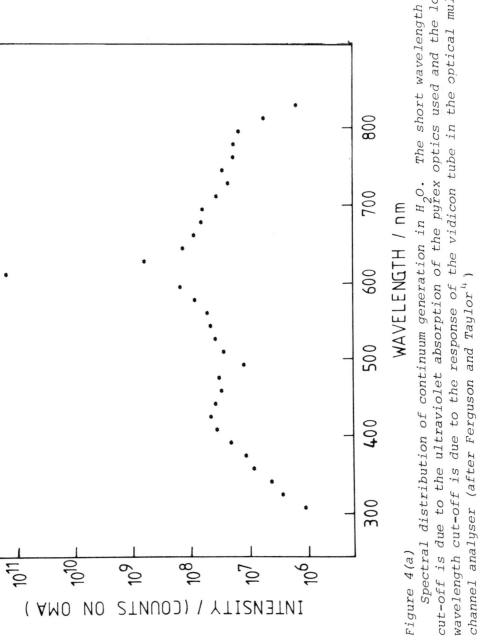

Figure 4(a)

Spectral distribution of continuum generation in H_2O. The short wavelength cut-off is due to the ultraviolet absorption of the pyrex optics used and the long wavelength cut-off is due to the response of the vidicon tube in the optical multi-channel analyser (after Ferguson and Taylor[4])

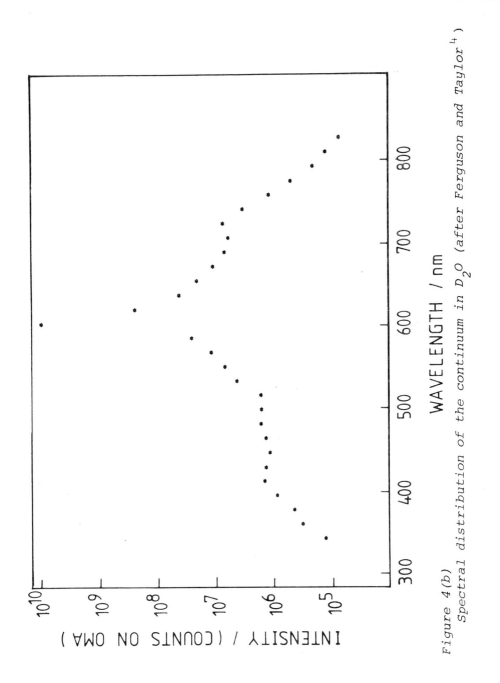

Figure 4(b)
Spectral distribution of the continuum in D_2O (after Ferguson and Taylor[4])

is converted into the Stokes or anti-Stokes beam and
the continuum is weak. The medium should be self-healing.
The threshold for continuum generation in most solids is
very close to or even in excess of the threshold for
optical damage. An excellent choice of continuum generator
is H_2O or D_2O. We have investigated many other liquids
such as benzene, ethanol, methanol, phosphoric acid and
trichloro-ethane. Each of these materials have slightly
different characteristics and for a particular purpose
may be superior to water but for general purposes we have
found H_2O or D_2O to be most satisfactory.

The spectral output of H_2O and D_2O continua are shown
in figure 4a,b. This was detected using a spectrometer
coupled to an optical multichannel analyser. The vertical
axis is the number of counts per channel of the analyser
plotted on a logarithmic scale. Both traces were taken at
approximately the same pump beam intensity of about 10^{11}
$W\ cm^{-2}$. It can be seen that the continuum in H_2O is about
an order of magnitude stronger than in D_2O but that the
D_2O spectrum is slightly smoother. In particular, the
H_2O spectrum shows a dip in the continuum at about 500nm
which is thought to be due to inverse stimulated Raman
scattering. In figure 4a,b the short wavelength limit is
set by the glass optics used and the long wavelength
cut-off is due to the fall in sensitivity of the optical
multi-channel analyser. With pulses of 1 psec in duration
at an energy of 1 mJ conversion efficiencies of between
5% and 10% have been obtained. We have measured duration

of the continuum by an autocorrelation technique and have
determined that the pulse duration is the same as that of
the exciting pulse and that, within the precision of the
measurements, the continuum is synchronous with the exciting
pulse.

Picosecond continuum generation techniques have recently
been extended into the femtosecond regime by Fork et al[20].
They amplify the output from a colliding pulse passively
mode-locked dye laser to a peak power of 1.2 GW as described
earlier. This beam is then focussed by reflecting optics
into a jet of ethylene glycol of 500 μm thickness. This
produces a power density at the focus of about 10^{13} - 10^{14}
W cm^{-2}. Fork et al[20] have measured the temporal characteristics of the continuum by measuring the cross-correlation
of the continuum and exciting beam in a mixing crystal. The
phase-matching angle was used to select a particular spectral
region of the continuuum for the cross-correlation. The
result of their experiment is shown in figure 5. This shows
the autocorrelation trace of the exciting pulse as a solid
line and gives the zero of time. Also shown, as dashed lines,
are the cross-correlations centred at 469.4nm and 1009.3nm.
The infrared and blue regions both have pulse durations which
closely approximate that of the pump pulse at 80 fsec. It
can be seen that the red portion of the continuum coincides
with the leading edge of the pump pulse whereas the blue
portion coincides with the trailing edge. This behaviour
is consistent with a model of the continuum generation process
in which self-phase modulation plays a prominent role. The

126

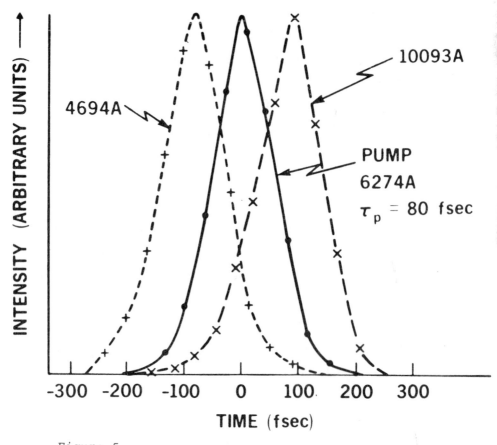

Figure 5

*Cross correlation traces for blue (+) and infrared (x)
portions of the continuum. An autocorrelation trace
of the pump pulse (O) at low intensity is also shown
(after Fork et al[20].*

rapid increase in intensity at the leading edge of the
pump pulse gives rise to a rapid increase in the refractive
index of the medium. This causes a rapid retardation of
the pump light and hence a shift in frequency to the red.
Similar arguments apply to the rapid fall in intensity
at the trailing edge of the pulse and predict a blue shift.

Figure 6 is a plot of the temporal distribution of the continuum as a function of frequency shift. The solid line is a smooth curve drawn through points which have been corrected for group velocity dispersion in the mixing crystal and in the continuum generating jet. This indicates that the temporal distribution of the continuum is taking place in the generation process itself and not simply due to group velocity dispersion.

It has also been shown by Fork *et al*[20] that a conversion efficiency of greater than 50% is possible with a stability sufficient to detect absorptions of as small as one part in ten thousand. The continuum in this case is so intense, of the order of 1GW, that it can itself be used to generate nonlinear phenomena. This thus provides a very valuable laser-like source of femtosecond pulses throughout the region from 190 nm to about 1.6 µm.

Conclusions

The rapid development of well behaved low energy picosecond and sub-picosecond light sources followed by amplification provides us with an extremely valuable source of intense light pulses. This opens up many areas in chemistry, biology and physics where large densities of excited states are to be studied or where nonlinear optical phenomena are important. We have described methods of producing a broad-band picosecond light source spanning the ultraviolet to infrared region. Many of these developments have taken

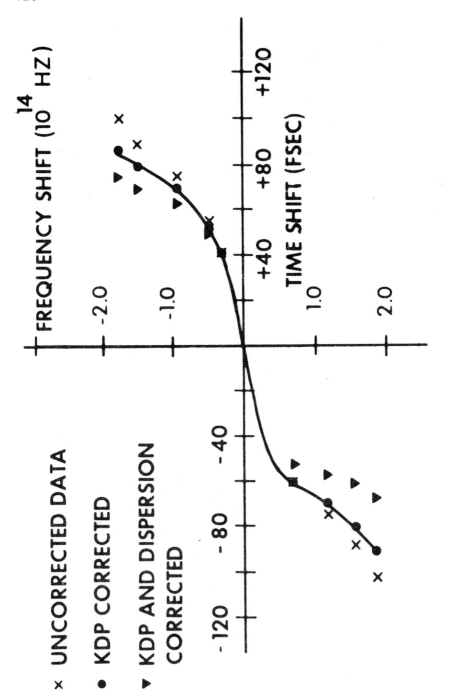

Figure 6 Plot of the continuum frequency shift versus time (after Fork et al[20])

place in physics laboratories but progressively these sources are being applied to problems in photochemistry and biology. It is likely that in the next few years we will see a very rapid growth in these methods.

Acknowledgements

The author wishes to thank all the members of the Picosecond Laboratory at the Clarendon Laboratory for many useful discussions. The financial support of SERC in the form of an Advanced Fellowship is gratefully acknowledged.

References

1. E.P. Ippen and C.V. Shank, *Picosecond Phenomena*, ed.
    C.V. Shank, E.P. Ippen and S.L.Shapiro, Springer
    Verlag, 103 (1978).

2. A. Migus, C.V. Shank, E.P. Ippen, R.L. Fork, *IEEE J.
    Quant. Electron.* QE18, 101 (1982).

3. A. Migus, J.L. Martin, R. Astier and A. Orszag,
    Picosecond Phenomena II, Springer Verlag, 59 (1980).

4. A.I. Ferguson and R.A. Taylor, *Proceedings of ECOSA '82,
    SPIE*, (1982).

5. P. Drell and S. Chu, *Optics Comm.* **28**, 343 (1979).

6. R. Wallenstein and T. W. Hänsch, *Optics Comm.* 14, 353
    (1975).

7. V. Ganiel, A. Hardy, G. Neumann and D. Treves, *IEEE
    J. Quant. Electron.,* QE11, 881 (1975).

8. R. Bellman, G. Birnbaum and W. G. Wagner, *J. Appl. Phys.*
    34, 780 (1963).

9. L.M. Frantz and J. S. Nodvik, *J. Appl. Phys.* 34, 2346
    (1963).

10. T.L. Koch, L.C. Chu and A. Yariv, *Optics Comm.* 40,364
    (1982).

11. T. Sizer II, J. D. Kafka, A. Krisiloff and G. Mourou,
    Optics Comm. **39**, 259 (1981).

12. R.L. Fork, B.I. Green and C.V. Shank, *Appl. Phys. Lett.*
    38, 671 (1981).

13. R.L. Fork, C.V. Shank and R.T. Yen, *Appl. Phys. Lett.*
    41,273 (1982).

14. E.B. Treacy, *IEEE J. Quant. Electron.*, **QE5**,454 (1969).

15. A. Penzkofer, A. Lauberau and W. Kaiser, *Phys. Rev. Lett.* **31**, 863 (1973).

16. A. Penzkofer, *Optics Comm.* **11**, 265 (1974).

17. A. Penzkofer, A. Seilmeier and W. Kaiser, *Optics Comm.*, **14**, 363 (1975).

18. W.L. Smith, P. Liu and N. Bloembergen, *Phys. Rev. A*, **15**, 2396 (1977).

19. D.K. Sharma and R.W. Yip, *Optics Comm.*, **30**,113 (1979).

20. R.L. Fork, C.V. Shank, R.T. Yen and C. Hirlimann, *Picosecond Phenomena III* ed. K.B. Eisenthal, R.M. Hochstrasser, W. Kaiser and A. Lauberau, Springer Verlag, 10 (1982).

Picosecond Synchronously Pumped Dye Laser Studies of Kinetics and Thermodynamics of a Gas Phase Exciplex

L.A. Chewter, D.V. O'Connor and D. Phillips*

Davy Faraday Research Lab., The Royal Institution, London, W1Z 4BS.

Picosecond pulses from synchronously pumped, mode locked, cavity dumped dye lasers are of great value in diminishing the instrument response function when used in conjunction with time correlated single photon counting for fluorescence detection. The stability of pulse profile obtained from such systems together with their high repetition rates are of great importance in that they allow the accurate fitting of complex decay functions such as those experienced in molecular excited state complex (exciplex) formation.

One such complex is formed in the gas phase between excited state α-cyanonaphthalene (CNN) and triethylamine (TEA). Fluorescence is observed from the excited state CNN and the complex itself which fluoresces visibly. Fluorescence decay times were measured using the time correlated single photon counting method in conjunction with laser excitation. Instrumental details have already been reported[1] and here only a brief summary is given. The excitation source was a mode locked synchronously pumped dye laser from which pulses were extracted at a 4MHz repetition rate using an acoustooptic cavity dumper. The pulses of visible radiation had a temporal width in the

order of 10ps and were frequency doubled to 305 nm using
an angle tuned ADP crystal. At this wavelength absorption
by the TEA is not observed. The sample fluorescence was
viewed at right angles to the excitation beam by focusing
onto the slits of a D330 Hilger Watts monochromator
where the wavelength resolved emission is detected by a
Mullard XP2020 Q fast high gain photomultiplier. Scattered
light was removed using a Melles Griot WG345 cutoff filter
before the monochromator. The time to amplitude converter
was operated in inverted mode in order to make use of the
total 4MHz laser repetition rate with the 'start' pulse
derived from a constant fraction discriminator triggered
by the photomultiplier pulse. Stop pulses were obtained
direct from a TTL logic circuit in the cavity dumper
driver electronics. At 305 nm the FWHM of the instrument
response was 600 ps and was independent of wavelength over
the wavelength range of emission studied here.

Decay curves were deconvoluted using a non-linear least
squares iterative reconvolution. The quality of the fit
was judged by values of the reduced chi-square (χ^2_ν) and
Durbin-Watson parameter (Serial correlation function) as
well as by visual inspection of plots of the weighted
residuals and the auto-correlation function of weighted
residuals. Data was accepted in general if the χ^2_ν was
less than 1.2, and the Durbin-Watson parameter was greater
than 1.5 or 1.75 for single and double exponential fitting
functions. However, data was also accepted if the χ^2_ν

was higher than 1.2 provided the other three criteria were satisfactory especially the residuals which gave a random distribution. It is important to note that all four criteria were used to judge the fit as no single parameter is in all cases sufficient.

Preparation of the gas phase samples has been described previously[2]. Concentrations in the order of 10^{-5} mole dm^{-3} in CNN with cyclohexane as a buffer gas at 3 atm and concentrations of the order of 10^{-3} mole dm^{-3} in TEA, were obtained in the gas phase. Fluorescence was observed at two emission wavelengths. At 350 nm fluorescence of the excited state CNN monomer was observed only and at 450 nm only fluorescence from the complex was observed. The fluorescence from both species was dual exponential with two decaying exponentials in the monomer fluorescence with a growth followed by a decay in the exciplex fluorescence as illustrated in Figures 1 and 2.

Table 1 shows the two 'lifetimes' associated with each decay along with pre-exponential factor data where a_1-a_4 are the pre-exponential factors in:

$$[A^*] = a_1 e^{-t/\tau_1} + a_2 e^{-t/\tau_2} \qquad \ldots \text{(1)}$$

$$[AQ^*] = a_3 e^{-t/\tau_1} - a_4 e^{-t/\tau_2} \qquad \ldots \text{(2)}$$

where $[A^*]$ and $[AQ^*]$ are the concentrations of monomer and exciplex respectively at time t after excitation.

Table 1   Decay time data for CNN-TEA gas phase exciplex at 188°C.

TEA x 10^{+3} moles dm^{-3}	Monomer[a]			Exciplex[b]			
	τ_1 ns	τ_2 ns	$\dfrac{a_1}{a_1 + a_2}$	τ_1 ns	τ_2 ns	a_3	a_4
0		24.1					
0.222	8.17	11.96	0.64	8.64	12.05	-0.46	0.46
0.530	5.41	10.13	0.82	5.80	11.60	-2.69	2.68
0.837	4.07	10.50	0.90	4.16	11.11	-3.68	3.70
2.13	2.00	11.23	0.98	1.96	10.97	-2.33	2.33
3.36	1.31	10.35	0.98	1.31	10.38	-1.93	1.92

136

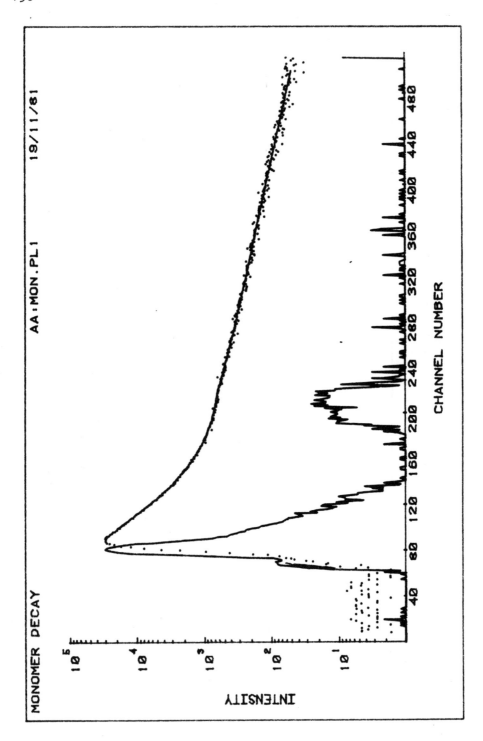

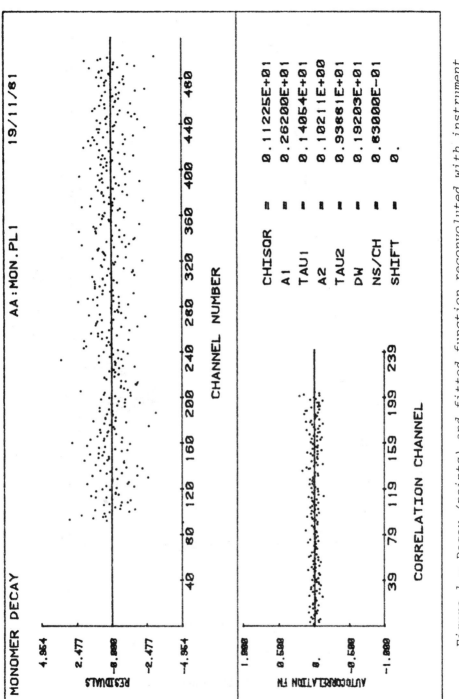

Figure 1 - Decay (points) and fitted function reconvoluted with instrument response for a typical monomer decay.

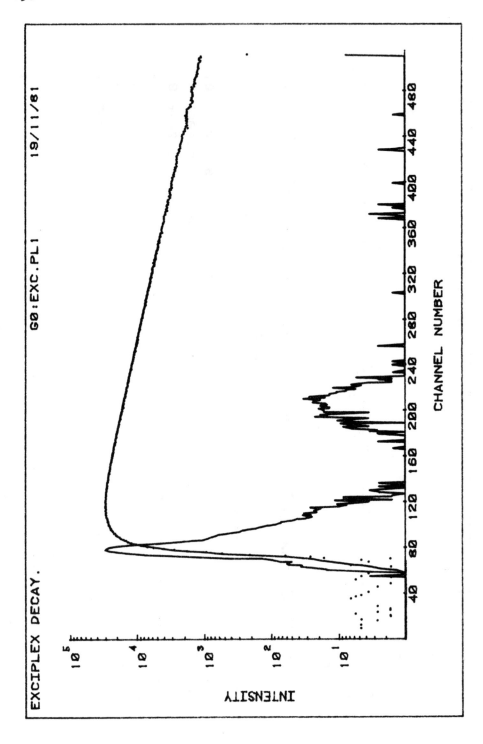

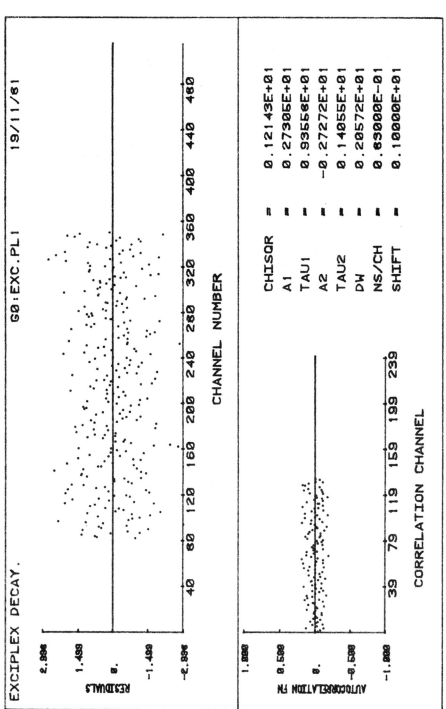

Figure 2 – Decay (points) and fitted function reconvoluted with instrument response for a typical exciplex decay.

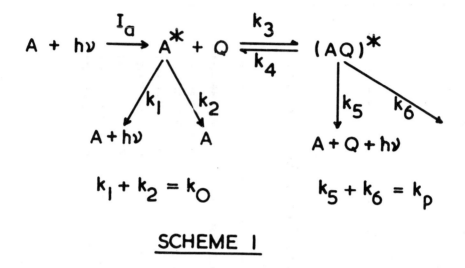

$$k_1 + k_2 = k_O \qquad k_5 + k_6 = k_p$$

SCHEME I

Exciplex kinetics in non polar solution can usually be described by the mechanism in Scheme 1 which predicts the time dependant concentration dependence of monomer and exciplex as given in equations (1) and (2) with

$$\lambda_{1,2} = \tfrac{1}{2}\big|k_0 + k_3\,[Q] + k_4 + k_p \pm \{(k_0 + k_3\,[Q] - k_4 - $$

$$k_p)^2 + 4k_3k_4[Q]\}^{\frac{1}{2}}\big| \quad \tau_1 = {}^1/\lambda_1 \ \ \tau_2 = {}^1/\lambda_2 \quad \ldots(3)$$

$$\frac{a_1}{a_1 + a_2} = \frac{k_0 + k_3[Q] - \lambda_2}{\lambda_1 - \lambda_2} \qquad \ldots(4)$$

$$-a_3 = a_4 = \frac{C\,k_5k_3[Q]}{\lambda_1 - \lambda_2} \qquad \ldots(5)$$

From Table 1 it can be seen that there is good agreement between τ_1 and τ_2 in both decays as predicted from Scheme 1. a_3 and a_4 which are independent variables in the fitting of the exciplex decay show excellent agreement with the prediction derived from equation (5) that they be equal in magnitude but opposite in sign.

From equation (3) the following two relationships may be deduced

$$\lambda_1 + \lambda_2 = k_0 + k_3[Q] + k_4 + k_p \qquad \ldots (6)$$

$$\lambda_1 \lambda_2 = k_0 (k_4 + k_p) + k_3 k_p [Q] \qquad \ldots (7)$$

which are plotted in Figure 3 using an average of values obtained from monomer and exciplex decays. Good straight lines are obtained from both plots and the rate constants obtained are given, along with rate constants obtained at four other temperatures, in Table 2.

It can be seen that the value of k_3, the rate constant for the quenching step, is of the order of magnitude expected for a gas kinetic hard sphere collision between CNN and TEA. Although the quality of the data is good the two values of k_4 show a discrepency which might be expected as they are obtained from the intercepts of plots of (6) and (7). k_4 obtained from equation (7) would probably be the more unreliable as errors are a product of these in λ_1 and

Table 2   Rate constants for CNN-TEA gas phase exciplex interpreted by Scheme 1 at various temperatures.

Temp °C	a $k_0 \times 10^{-7}$ S^{-1}	$k_3 \times 10^{-11}$ M^{-1} S^{-1}	$k_p \times 10^{-7}$ S^{-1}	b $k_4 \times 10^{-7}$ S^{-1}	c $k_4 \times 10^{-7}$ S^{-1}
180	4.19	2.17	9.34	1.79	3.18
188	4.20	2.08	9.60	2.10	3.50
200	4.31	1.99	9.65	3.14	5.90
211	4.38	1.86	10.75	3.88	5.84
220	4.47	1.73	11.56	5.13	8.06

a) $1/T_0$ measured from unquenched CNN

b)   from plot of $\lambda_1 + \lambda_2$ vs [Q]

c)   from plot of $\lambda_1\lambda_2$ vs [Q]

λ_2 and k_4 is not directly obtained from the intercept. In order to test the validity of the pre-exponential factors a_1 and a_2 a plot of equation (4) is given in Figure 4. A linear plot is obtained from which a value for k_3 is extracted of 2.04×10^{11} M^{-1} s^{-1} which is in excellent agreement with the value given in Table 1.

Scheme 1 predicts linear Stern-Volner plots from which an overall quenching rate constant, k_q, given by

$$k_q = \frac{k_3 k_p}{k_4 + k_p}$$

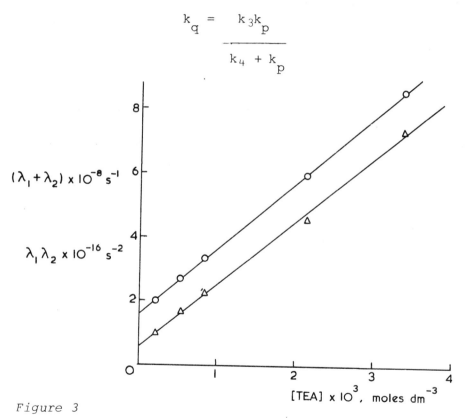

Figure 3

Plot of $\lambda_1 + \lambda_2$ (o) and $\lambda_1 \lambda_2$ (Δ) vs TEA at $188^{\circ}C$.

can be calculated. Table 3 gives the values of k_q calculated from values of rate constants in Table 1 along with k_q obtained directly from steady state measurements[3]. Good agreement is obtained using the more reliable values of k_4 from the plot of equation (6) while as expected, the value of k_4 from the plot of equation (7) shows some discrepancy. Such good agreement confirms the validity of scheme 1 and also appears to justify that belief that the lack of agreement between steady state and transient data in many solution exciplex studies is a result of distortions associated with transient effects in diffusion controlled reactions.

Table 3

Values of k_q the quenching rate constant from transient and steady state data.

Temp	[a] k_q x 10^{-11} $M^{-1} S^{-1}$	[b] k_q x 10^{-11} $M^{-1} S^{-1}$	[c] k_q x 10^{-11} $M^{-1} S^{-1}$
180	1.80	1.82	1.62
188	1.67	1.71	1.52
200	1.51	1.50	1.23
211	1.35	1.33	1.20
220	1.22	1.20	1.02

a) from steady state measurements

b) calculated from k_3, k_p and k_4 from $\lambda_1 + \lambda_2$ vs [Q] plot

c) calculated from k_3, k_p and k_4 from $\lambda_1\lambda_2$ vs [Q] plot

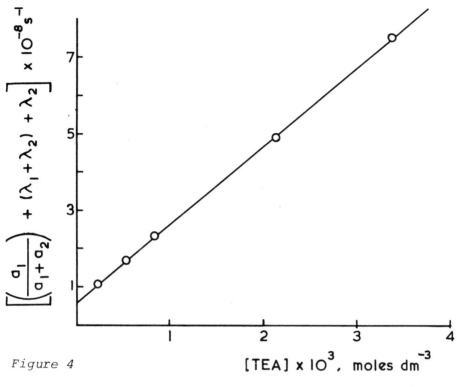

Figure 4

Plot of $(a_1/(a_1 + a_2))$ $(\lambda_1 - \lambda_2) + \lambda_2$ vs TEA at $188^{o}C$.

From the values of rate constants ΔS and ΔH values
for exiplex formation were obtained[4] as -52.7 joule mol^{-1}
and 49.0 K joule mol^{-1} respectively which correspond to
orders of magnitude found in other exciplex systems[5-8].

It can be seen that when picosecond techniques are
used on systems with complex decay functions deconvolution
techniques may be applied very successfully to yield
reliable high quality data from which many predictions

about kenetic schemes may be verified. All the parameters
in the fitting of such functions are reliable and

instrumental in the verification of the kinetic model
and derivation of rate constants and thermodynamic data.

References

1. R.A. Lampert, L.A. Chewter, D. Phillips, D.V. O'Connor, A.J. Roberts and S.R. Meech. *Anal. Chem.,* 55,68 (1983).

2. D.V. O'Connor, L. Chewter and D. Phillips. *J. Phys. Chem.,* **86**, 3400 (1982).

3. L.A. Chewter, D.V. O'Connor and D. Phillips. *Chem. Phys. Lett.,* **84**,39 (1981).

4. L.A. Chewter, D.V. O'Connor and D. Phillips. *J. Phys. Chem.,* Submitted.

5. M. Itoh and Y. Hamishima, *Chem. Phys. Letter.,* **83**,405 (1981).

6. A. Davis, M.J. Pilling, M.J. Westby. *J. Chem. Phys.,* **63**, 209 (1981).

7. D.V. O'Connor and W.R. Ware. *J.A.C.S.,* 101, 121 (1979).

8. S. Hirayama. *Int.J. Quanta. Chem.,* **18**, 257 (1980).

Fast Isomerizations and Conformational Changes in Ground- and Excited States of Cyanine and TPM Molecules, Studied by Picosecond Absorption Techniques

Villy Sundström and Tomas Gillbro

*Division of Physical Chemistry, University of Umeå,
S-901 87 Umeå, Sweden*

Abstract

Detailed studies of the picosecond relaxation kinetics in polymethine and TPM dyes have allowed us to present models for isomerization and conformational changes in ground- and electronically excites states of the molecules.

An experimental apparatus, based on a sync-pumped cavity-dumped picosecond dye laser and a Pockels cell modulated CW dye laser, capable of measuring transient absorption difference spectra on the picosecond time-scale is also described.

Introduction

Time-resolved absorption measurements with picosecond time-resolution have evolved along two basically different lines. On the one hand there are the techniques relying on high-power laser pulses generated at low repetition rates in solid state lasers. Fundamental, harmonic or Raman shifted wavelengths of these lasers are employed for excitation of the samples and the 'white light continuum' or picosecond dye laser pulses are the sources of probe light of widely varying wavelengths[1-4]. The possibility of independently tuning pump and probe wavelengths and thus obtaining difference spectra is the strength of this method. Due to the relatively low signal to noise ratio available with this technique it is less suited for precise kinetic measurements.

Using continuously operating, sync-pumped or passively modelocked dye lasers is an alternative way of performing absorption experiments. The high pulse repetition rate of these systems combined with phase-sensitive detection results in a superior signal-to-noise ratio[5-7]. These laser systems are therefore ideally suited for very precise kinetic measurements with the capability of resolving multiple exponential decays with small difference in rate constants[8]. The broad spectral tuning range of sync-pumped dye lasers is another valuable characteristic in these measurements. Although tunable over a wide range, there has been an important limitation in the use of these laser systems; both excitation and analyzing pulses are generated by the same dye laser and consequently of identical wavelengths. For the particular molecule being investigated this restricts the available wavelength interval to that where the molecules absorb. Measurements with this type of equipment, performed in the past, have therefore been limited to yield only kinetic information.

Recently Ippen *et al* proposed a method[9] based on frequency up-conversion of CW or long-pulsed analyzing light produced in a laser independent of the picosecond laser to overcome these problems. Two experiments with this technique have been published[10,11], but the experimental details did not allow measurements of difference spectra at that time. Now, we have improved this technique to allow the recording of both difference spectra and absolute absorption spectra of pico-second transients[12].

Polymethine- and triphenyl methane dyes are two classes of molecules which have attracted a great deal of interest from picosecond spectroscopists, due to their very interesting photophysical properties and their use as laser and mode-locking dyes. The radiationless relaxations of these molecules have been shown to be strongly viscosity and temperature dependent[13-15]. Torsional movements in the excited states are generally considered as inducing mechanism for the relaxations[15-16]. We have used our picosecond absorption spectrometer to perform a detailed study of the relaxation processes in these molecules, and some of the results that we have obtained will be presented here. The paper is structured in the following way. In section II we will describe the latest development of the picosecond absorption spectrometer, i.e., the use of an independently tunable analyzing light which enables us to record transient absorption spectra. This technique is used to obtain absorption spectra and quantum yields of pinacyanol and cyanine photoisomers produced by picosecond pulse excitation. In section III we will present some of our results on the picosecond kinetics of polymethine and TPM dyes, and suggest plausible models to account for our observations.

The Experimental Technique

Figure 1 schematically illustrates the experimental arrangement of this new technique. A synchronously pumped, cavity-dumped dye laser (DL1) produces picosecond pulses (2-8 ps FWHM) which are used both to excite the sample and as pump in the sum-frequency generation in the non-linear crystal. The analyzing light is generated in a CW dye laser (DL2) pumped by a 4 W Ar^+ laser (AL2). Normally, an average power of 50 - 100 mW out from DL2 is used. To reduce the power incident on the sample the analyzing beam is modulated by a Pockels cell (PC) into a train of *ca* 20 ns long pulses synchronized at the sample to the picosecond pulses by means of an electric delay line of proper length. At a repetition rate of 400 kHz an average power of typically 0.2 mW pulsed output is measured after the Pockels cell. This corresponds to a pulse energy of *ca* 0.5 nJ which is *ca* a factor of ten lower than the excitation pulse energy. The pulse length (*ca* 20 ns) of the analyzing pulse is long enough that the intensity at its maximum can be considered constant during the time intervals of interest,

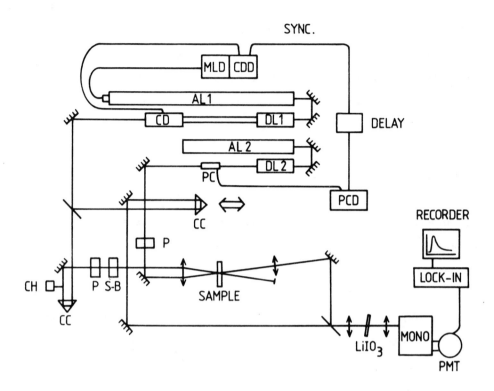

Figure 1

    Experimental arrangement for measuring absorption difference spectra with picosecond time-resolution. AL1 = mode-locked Ar⁺ laser, AL2 = CW Ar⁺ laser, DL1 = sync-pumped dye laser, DL2 = CW dye laser, CD = cavity dumper, CDD = cavity dumper driver, MLD = mode locker driver, PC = Pockels cell, PCD = Pockels cell driver, Delay = electric delay for
    synchronization of ps and ns pulses,
CC = corner cube prism, P = prism polarizer,
S - B = Soleil - Babinet compensator, CH = mechanical
    chopper,
PMT = photomultiplier.

0-2 ns. As a consequence of the wavelength dependent half-wave voltage of the Pockels cell the polarization direction of the Pockels cell output varies with wavelength. It is well known that absorption recovery measurements utilizing linearly polarized light are sensitive to the polarization directions of the pump and probe beams, through the effect of rotational relaxation. To avoid distortions of the measured kinetics, caused by the varying polarization direction, the polarization is fixed by a prism polarizer placed after the Pockels cell. A polarizer and a Soleil-Babinet compensator are also used in the excitation beam to facilitate any desired rotation of the plane of polarization. The 20 ns analyzing pulses view the absorbance change in the sample caused by the picosecond excitation pulses. The sum-frequency signal between the analyzing pulses and a small part of the ps-pulses is finally generated in a $LiIO_3$ or KDP crystal and detected by a monochromator, photomultiplier and a lock-in amplifier. The magnitude of the sum-frequency signal, which is proportional to the transmission change in the sample in the small signal limit, depends on a number of different factors such as excitation and crystal pump pulse intensity, analyzing light intensity, sample absorbance, nonlinear crystal efficiency for sum-frequency generation and detection system sensitivity at a particular wavelength. Since the instrument is a single beam instrument the measured sum-frequency signals have to be properly normalized at every wavelength in order to obtain a correct difference spectrum.

To demonstrate the usefulness of this technique we will show results from two different kinds of problems particularly well suited to be studied with this method.

a) Formation of transient species

Upon picosecond pulse excitation of cyanine dyes such as pinacyanol and 1,1'-diethyl-4,4'-cyanine iodide (cyanine) in low viscosity solvents transients having lifetimes on the order of 10 ns are formed[17]. With the technique described above we have obtained the difference spectra, see figure 2, and quantum yields of these transients. It is evident that upon excitation, a species having a red-shifted absorption spectrum is formed. For pinacyanol/MeOH a transient with λ_{max}^{iso} = 632 ± 1 nm and lifetime $\tau \sim$ 10 ns is formed with a yield of ϕ = 0.04. The corresponding figures to cyanine are λ_{max}^{iso} = 621 ± 1 nm, $\tau \sim$ 10 ns and ϕ = 0.2.

In the literature there are numerous observations of photoisomer formation in polymethine dyes[18-21]. There are examples of unstable isomers having red-shifted as well as blue-shifted absorption spectra relative that of the stable isomers. Lifetimes ranging from milliseconds to fractions of microseconds have been reported. Thus, it seems very likely that the red-shifted transients observed by us in pinacyanol and cyanine are due to very unstable photoisomers.

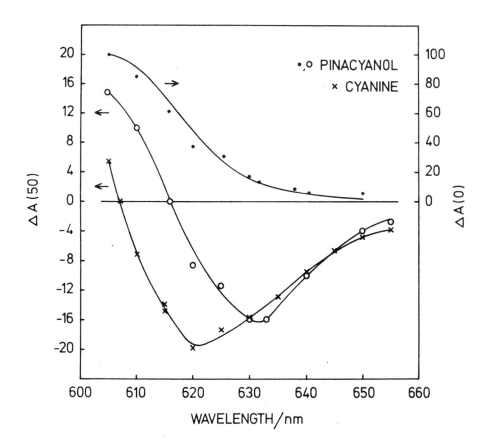

Figure 2

Measured difference spectra of pinacyanol/MeOH and
cyanine/EtOH at $\tau \approx 0$ ps, $\Delta A(0)$ and $\tau \approx 50$ ps, $\Delta A(50)$.
The solid line through $\Delta A(0)$ of pinacyanol is the
conventional absorption spectrum normalized to the
measured ΔA at the absorption maximum, λ_{max} = 605 nm.
ΔA is in arbitrary units.

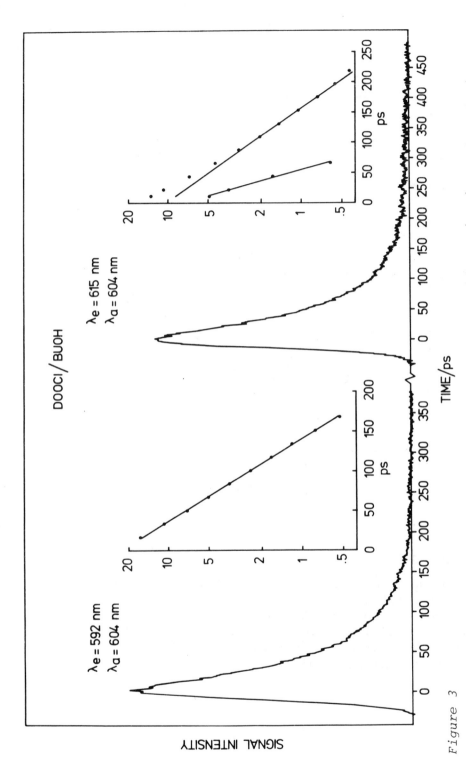

Figure 3

Kinetic measurements on DQOCl/BuOH using independently tunable excitation and analyzing light.

b)   Multiple exponential decays

In cases where two kinetic components with small differences
in rate constant (a factor of 2-3) are present it is often
difficult to distinguish them and obtain reliable values of
rate coefficients and intensity ratios.   In unfavourable cases
two exponential decays may come out as a single exponential
having a lifetime which is approximately the average of two
components[8].   If there are two different species absorbing
at slightly different wavelengths causing the double
exponential decay the technique described above can be very
useful in distinguishing the two separate decay components.
This is demonstrated in figure 3 in the case of DQOCI in
butanol.   DQOCI is excited at two different wavelengths, λ_e
= 592 nm close to the absorption maximum and λ_e = 615 nm in
the red wing of the absorption spectrum.   The resulting
kinetics are analyzed at λ_a = 604 nm.   It is seen that upon
changing the exciting wavelength from 592 to 615 nm the
recorded kinetics change from a single exponential (τ= 48 ps)
to a double exponential with τ_1 = 20 ps and τ_2 = 50 ps.
These results indicate the presence of two groundstate
species in DQOCI having slightly differing absorption spectra.
Examination of a molecular model of the space-filling type
of DQOCI, suggests that the benzoxazole ring should be very
free to rotate around the 2-8 C-C bond.   The two possible
planar conformations which results as a consequence of such
a ring rotation seem to have rather similar groundstate
energies as judged from the amount of steric hindrance
present in the two conformations.   Consequently it seems

reasonable to assign the two measured lifetimes (τ_1 = 20 ps and τ_2 = 50 ps) to the groundstate recovery of these two conformations of the DQOCI molecule.

Photophysics of polymethine and triphenylmethane (TPM) dyes
a) Polymethine dyes

The photophysical and photochemical properties of polymethine dyes have been studied intensively for several decades using both stationary and time-resolved spectro-scopic techniques. It is the viscosity and temperature dependent radiationless processes in particular, that have attracted much interest. The general observation for a solution of these dyes is a strongly viscosity and temperature dependent fluorescence quantum yield, or excited state lifetime[5,13,14]. The viscosity dependence of the fluorescence quantum yield or excited state lifetime is often reported to be close to either $\eta^{2/3}$ or η^{1}, and accordingly interpreted in terms of either of two models, the Forster-Hoffmann (FH)[15] or the Oster-Nishijima model (ON)[16], predicting the above mentioned viscosity dependence. Both models consider a torsional motion of part of the molecule in the excited state as the inducing factor for the radiationless relaxations. ON describe the torsion as a free rotation whereas FH consider a motion damped by the surrounding solvent. A Kramers equation, for the rate of passage over a potential barrier of a particle subject to the irregular forces of surrounding solvent molecules, has very recently been applied[22-25] to the problem of conformational relaxation. This model requires that the relaxing molecules are trapped in a potential well deep enough that they are maintained in a quasi-equilibrium state. In other words, the intra-molecular barrier, E_a, towards conformational change in the excited state has to be large compared to kT. According to the Kramers equation the viscosity dependence of the relaxation rate varies from case to case and one might in principle find any type of viscosity dependence between η^0 and η^1.

Our observations on the polymethine photophysics in solution[5,17] can be summarized in the following points:

i) Following picosecond excitation to the S_1 there is efficient radiationless deactivation (on the picosecond time-scale) of the excited state.

ii) The measured rate constants, k_{obsd}, obey the relation $k_{obsd} = C \cdot \eta^{-\alpha}$, where C is a constant of proportionality and η is the viscosity of the solvent. The parameter α varies in the range 0.4 to 1.1 and is sensitive to the particular dye molecule being studied and the nature of the solvent[5].

iii) Photoisomers are formed to some extent in most polymethines that we have studied [17], see also section II. The isomerization quantum yield, ϕ_{iso}, is highly viscosity dependent

iv) The observed relaxation rates have no measurable activation energy in excess of that caused by the temperature dependence of solvent viscosity[17].

These observations can be accounted for by using the potential-surface diagram of figure 4. The molecules excited to n-S_1 are de-activated through two different radiationless processes, one direct internal conversion back to the ground state, n-S_0, with rate constant k_{ic} and a conformational change with rate constant k_p leading to a twisted excited electronic state, t-S_2. The measured rate constant, k_{obsd}, is the sum of these two constants; thus, $k_{obsd} = k_{ic} + k_p$. Of the molecules reaching t-S_2, a certain ratio will complete the conformational change and end up in the ground state of the photo-isomer, p-S_0. The rest of the molecules will relax back to the normal-form ground state, n-S_0. The ratio between the number of molecules that isomerize and return to n-S_0 from t-S_2 is given by k''_p/k'_p. By a thermally activated process the isomerized molecules are brought back to the stable isomer ground state, n-S_0. Using this model we will now discuss the points i-iv in some more detail.

The macroscopic viscosity alone is no good parameter in describing the viscosity dependence of k_{obsd}; this is immediately evident from figure 5 where pinacyanol/hexanol (η = 4.8 cP) has a longer lifetime, τ = 54 ps, then has pinacyanol/glycerol-water 61.4% (w/w) (η = 11.6 cP), τ = 30 ps. This trend becomes particularly evident when the measured lifetimes of pinacyanol in a series of n-alcohols and a series of glycerol-water mixtures are plotted vs viscosity

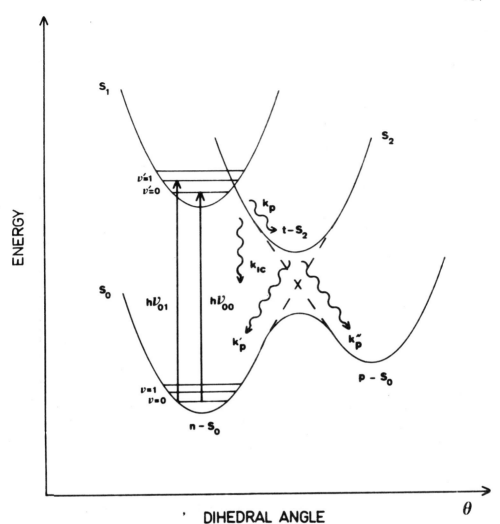

Figure 4

Model used to discuss the photophysics of the studied polymethine molecules. n⁻S₀ and p-S₀ are the normal and photoisomer ground states respectively and t-S₂ is the twisted excited state.

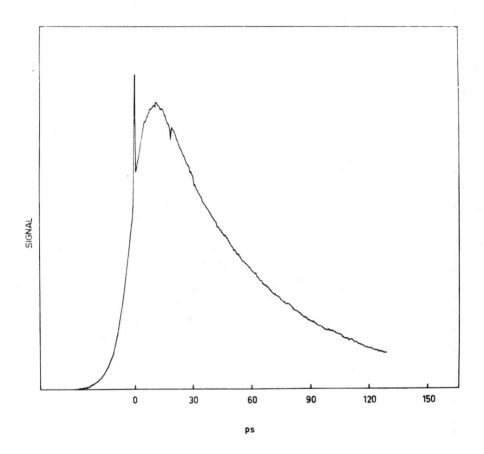

Figure 5

　　Recorded absorption recovery kinetics of pinacyanol at 619nm in:

　　a)　hexanol at 296 K, τ = 54 ps
　　b)　glycerol-water 61.4% (w#w) at 296 K, τ = 30 ps.

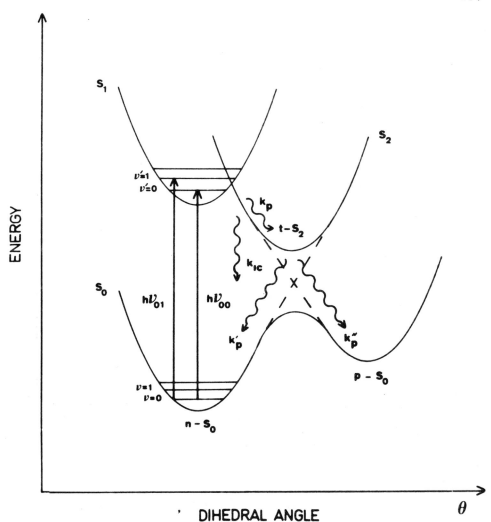

Figure 4

Model used to discuss the photophysics of the studied polymethine molecules. n^-S_0 and $p-S_0$ are the normal and photoisomer ground states respectively and $t-S_2$ is the twisted excited state.

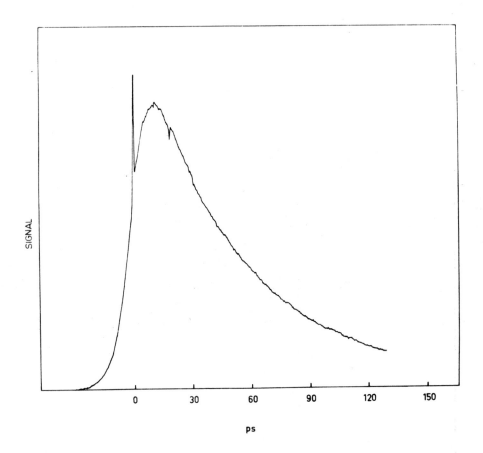

SIGNAL

ps

Figure 5

Recorded absorption recovery kinetics of pinacyanol
at 619nm in:
a)   hexanol at 296 K, τ = 54 ps
b)   glycerol-water 61.4% (w#w) at 296 K, τ = 30 ps.

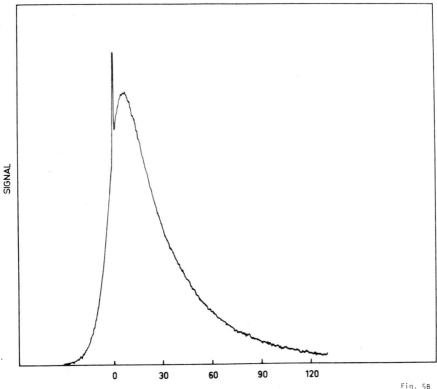

SIGNAL

0   30   60   90   120

ps

Fig. 5B

see figure 6. It is seen that the viscosity dependence, as
reflected by the parameter α, is considerably stronger in
n-alcohol solutions than in glycerol-water or glycerol-
methanol solutions. The reasons for this might be two-fold.
Firstly, by considering our model in figure 4 it is clear
that k_{obsd} could vary in the way described above if k_{ic} and
k_p differ in their viscosity dependencies and the ratio of
molecules going either way is different in n-alcohol and
glycerol-containing solutions. If this is true there would
be a parallel trend in the amount of photoisomer being
formed. As will be shown below, the isomerization quantum
yield largely follows η^{-1} and moreover k_p is in most cases
considerably lower than k_{ic}, so small relative variations
are unlikely to produce an appreciable variation in α.

A more likely explanation is that α is determined by the
local microviscosity around the dye molecule. It is not
unreasonable to think that there might be a considerable
difference in microviscosity in a n-alcohol and glycerol-
water solution. There are some recent measurements[26,27]
of rotational relaxation rates of R6G in glycerol and
ethyleneglycol solutions indicating deviations from
Stokes-Einstein behaviour. Although these measurements
were performed on a xanthene dye which is structurally
different from the polymethines studied by us, these
results might be taken as an indication of the microviscosity being lower in a glycerol-water or glycerol-methanol
solution than in a solution of n-alcohol of the same

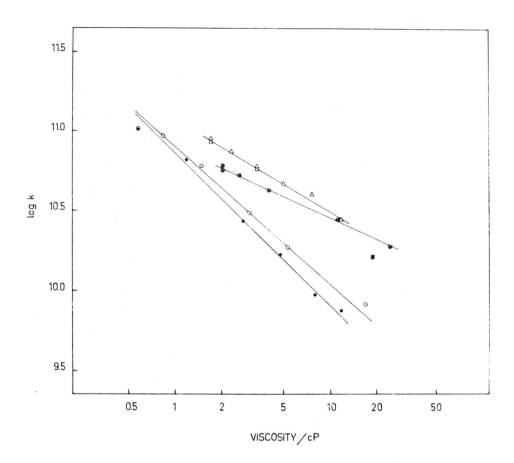

Figure 6

    Rate constants of pinacyanol relaxation as a function
of viscosity in various solvents.

● *n-alcohols at 597 nm, α = 0.91*
☉ *methanol at 595 nm, α = 0.79*
⊗ *glycerol-methanol at 596 nm, α = 0.45*
△ *glycerol-water at 597 nm, α = 0.57*
■ *ethyleneglycol at 595 nm, 296 K*
α *is the slope of the fitted straight lines.*

macroscopic viscosity. The α-value measured by us will consequently be lower in the former type of solution. Several other polymethine dyes have been studied and they all show similar behaviour[5]. These results strongly suggest that neither of the FH or ON models describes the relaxation processes properly. A good model must predict the large variations in α. The above mentioned Kramers equation accomplishes this, but as will be shown below there are other problems associated with this approach.

The strong viscosity and temperature dependence of the isomerization yield is illustrated by the results for pinacyanol and cyanine in figure 7. The method of viscosity variation has little influence on the isomerization yield, as shown in figure 7 identical results are obtained when the viscosity is varied by lowering the temperature and changing the composition of a glycerol-methanol solution at room temperature, respectively. This suggests that there is no significant activation energy for the isomerization process. An 'iso-viscosity plot' for pinacyanol using butanol (T = 298 K, η = 2.6 cP), ethanol (T = 256 K) and methanol (T = 217 K) yields an activation energy indistinguishable from zero. Thus, there seem to be very low activation energy barriers in the excited state. This is an important experimental result which tells us that the relaxation processes of these molecules can probably not be described by the Kramers equation, which requires a quasi-equilibrium in the excited state.

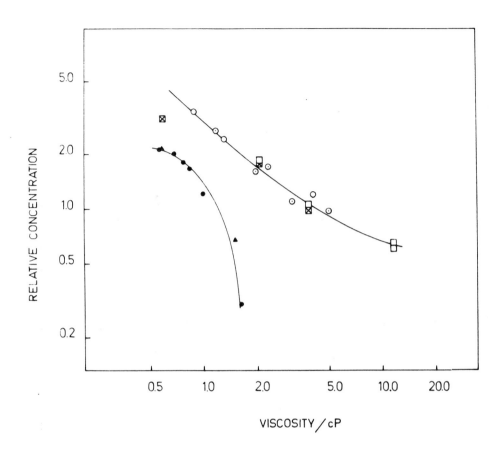

Figure 7

    Relative concentration of photoisomers as a function
of viscosity, no matter the method of viscosity variation.
Upper curve is cyanine: O *586 nm EtOH;* ⊙ *588 nm EtOH;*
□ *597 nm glycerol/MeOH;*⊠*585 nm glycerol/MeOH*
Lower curve is pinacyanol:▲*595 nm MeOH;* ● *619 nm MeOH*
The pinacyanol curve has been scaled by multiplication
with a factor 10.   Units of concentration are arbitrary
units.

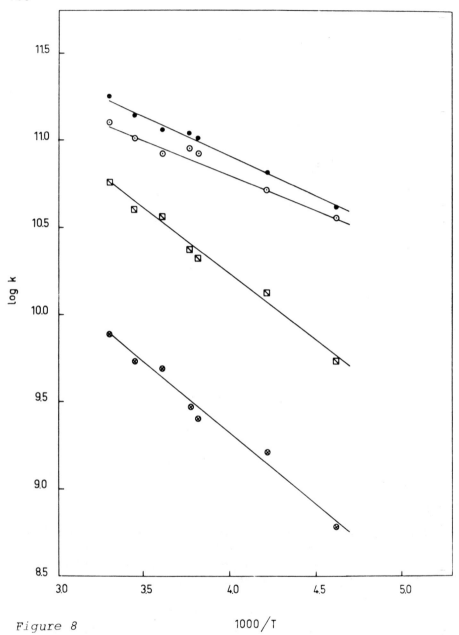

Figure 8   1000/T

Temperature dependence of k_{ic} and k_p for pinacyanol in methanol at 619 nm. Upper two lines are k_{ic}:
● $\gamma = 1$; ○ $\gamma = 0.1$. *Lower two lines are k_p:*
○ $\gamma = 1$; ▣ $\gamma = 0.1$.

The viscosity dependence of the isomerization yield can
most easily be rationalized by our model in figure 4 if k_{ic}
and k_p have differing viscosity dependencies. Then, the
observed rate constant k_{obsd} can be decomposed into its
constituents, k_{ic} and k_p. This is illustrated in the case
of pinacyanol/MeOH in figure 8. It is obvious that the
rates of the two radiationless processes differ in their
temperature and viscosity dependencies; k_p is seen to have
a considerably stronger viscosity dependence than has k_{ic}.
Since we do not know the value of the branching parameter,
$\gamma = k''_p/(k'_p + k''_p)$, we have plotted the results of figure
8 for $\gamma = 1$ and $\gamma = 0.1$, respectively, to demonstrate the
effect of varying γ. As expected, a high γ-value results in
a low rate of conformational change, k_p. Very similar
results to those of figure 8 are obtained for other polymethine dyes[17].

b) TPM dyes
The TPM dyes are another class of dye molecules which has
been extensively studied through the years[2,15,16,28-30].
Like the polymethine dyes they display highly efficient
radiationless relaxations which quenches the fluorescence
emission to such an extent that even under laser excitation
some dyes are apparently non-fluorescent. The quantum
yield of fluorescence and excited state lifetimes are
strongly viscosity and temperature dependent. Experimental
results are generally interpreted in terms of the FH model[15]
which assumes strongly displaced energy minima in the ground

170

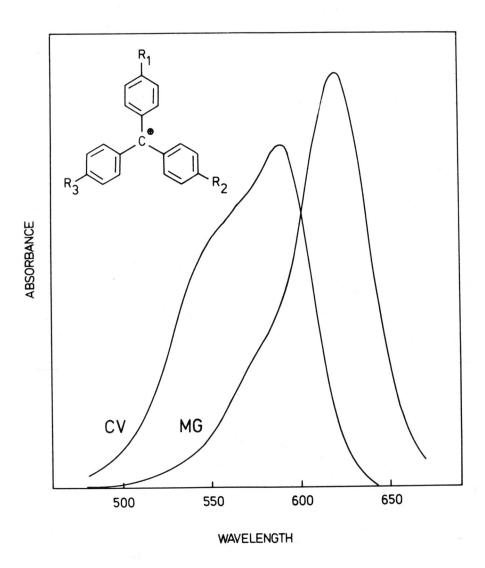

Figure 9

Structures of studied TPM molecules and absorption spectra of crystal violet and malachite green in ethanol.

and excited states due to different double bond character
in the two states. A molecule excited to S_1 is driven
by the intramolecular potential towards a new equilibrium
position having a high rate of radiationless relaxation.
This is thought to take place through a synchronous
rotation of the phenyl rings about the bond joining each
ring and the central carbon atom. The viscous drag of
the solvent hinders this rotation. High solvent viscosity
therefore results in a high fluorescence quantum yield.
A fluorescence quantum yield varying as $\eta^{2/3}$ is predicted
by the model. Experimentally, values close to this have
often been reported in highly viscous solutions[15,30].

In solvents of low viscosity the radiationless
relaxation rate of these molecules is extremely fast.
Such dye/solvent systems have consequently escaped from
a more systematic study. In order to get a comprehensive
picture of the relaxation kinetics of the TPM dyes we have
performed a thorough study of several dyes in n-alcohol
and glycerol-water solutions[31]. The structure of the
studied molecules and two representative absorption
spectra are shown in figure 9. The photophysical properties
of the TPM dyes are quite complex and have several different
aspects[31]. Nevertheless, our observations can be summarized
in the following points.

i)   The measured absorption recovery kinetics in n-alcohol
     solutions at a particular wavelength can in most cases

be fitted to a double exponential decay, with lifetimes τ_1 and τ_2. For some dyes (CV,EV and PF) τ_1 and τ_2 are seen to be wavelength dependent, while for MG and BG the lifetimes are constant over the entire wavelength region studied. In the former case the observations can be divided into three wavelength intervals according to their common appearance; at a particular wavelength called the isosbestic wavelength (λ_{iso}), which is specified by the particular dye/alcohol studied, the recorded kinetics collapses into a single exponential with lifetime τ_1; for $\lambda > \lambda_{iso}$ a double exponential with an initial fast recovery (τ_1) to a negative signal level followed by a slower decay (τ_2) of the negative signal is observed, a double exponential is also seen for $\lambda < \lambda_{iso}$, but here both τ_1 and τ_2 are positive signal components. For sufficiently short wavelengths τ_1 and τ_2 in addition become approximately a factor of two longer than for $\lambda > \lambda_{iso}$. These features are illustrated by the kinetic measurements on CV/HexOH in figure 10 and by the summary of kinetic parameters for CV and EV in Table I and II.

ii)   By comparing the absorption spectrum of a molecule displaying wavelength dependent relaxation times (CV for example) with the spectrum of a molecule lacking this dependence (MG for example) it is evident that the latter does not have the pronounced short-wavelength shoulder. Consequently

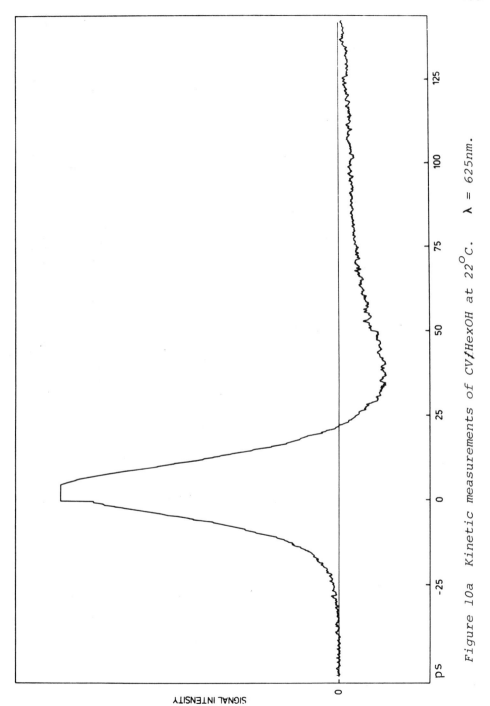

SIGNAL INTENSITY

0

ps

Figure 10a Kinetic measurements of CV/HexOH at 22°C.   λ = 625nm.

174

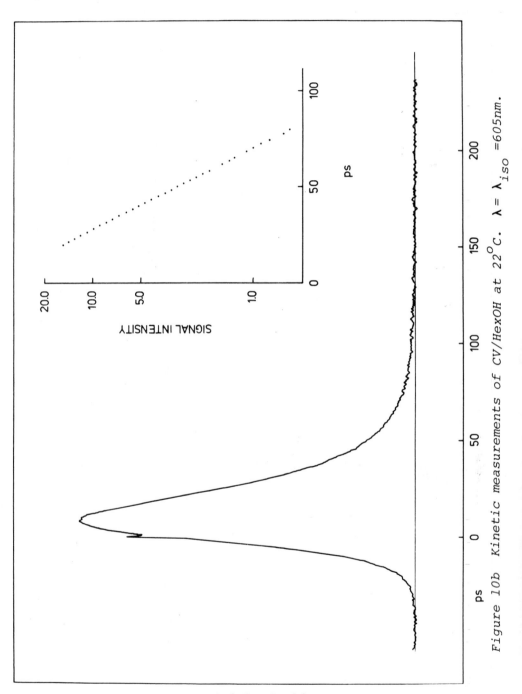

Figure 10b   Kinetic measurements of CV/HexOH at 22°C. $\lambda = \lambda_{iso} = 605nm$.

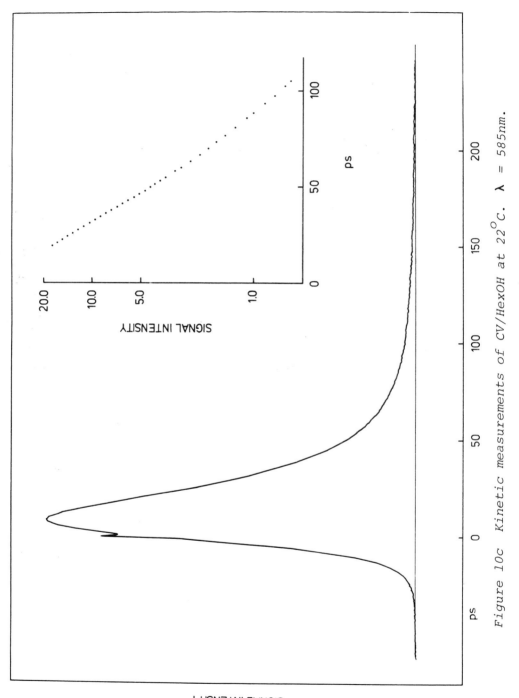

SIGNAL INTENSITY

Figure 10c Kinetic measurements of CV/HexOH at 22°C. λ = 585nm.

Table 1[a] CV/n-alcohols, kinetic parameters at different wavelengths and room temperature $23 \pm 1°C$

ROH	η/cp	τ_1 (ps)	τ_2 (ps)	A_1/A_2	λ_{iso} (nm)
			$\lambda = 625$ nm		
Ethanol	1.16	–	–	~ -1	599
Butanol	2.7	7.6	13.3	-2.3	603
Hexanol	4.8	9.3	29.6	-4.0	606
Octanol	8.0	11.5	50	-8.3	610
Decanol	11.7	14.4	105	~ -15	612

Table 11[a] EV/n-alcohols, kinetic parameters at different wavelengths and room temperature $23 \pm 1°C$

ROH	η/cp	τ_1 (ps)	τ_2 (ps)	A_1/A_2	λ_{iso} (nm)
			$\lambda = 625$ nm		
Methanol	0.58	–	–	–	599
Ethanol	1.16	6.8	10.7	–	605
Butanol	2.7	13.5	18.0	-1.5	611
Hexanol	4.8	15.2	63	-7.2	613
Octanol	8.0	22.3	128	-17	615
Decanol	11.7	31.3	330	-25	617

(a) The lifetimes reported in this table are averages of several measurements; the error limits, represented by scatter in the data, are ca $\pm 10\%$.

| τ_{iso} (ps) | $\lambda = 585$ nm | | $\lambda = 550$ nm | |
	τ_1 (ps)	τ_2 (ps)	τ	λ_{max} (nm)
3.7	9.0	–	–	589
7.2	13.8	–	13.2	591
12.0	22	–	18.6	593
17.4	28	114	27	594
19.0	33	212	32	597

| τ_{iso} (ps) | $\lambda = 585$ nm | | $\lambda = 550$ nm | |
	τ_1 (ps)	τ_2 (ps)	τ	λ_{max} (nm)
4.1	–	–	–	589
5.9	10.5	–	10.1	591
16.1	19	–	19	593
19.0	32	123	28	594
30	48	176	39	596
42	62	–	49	598

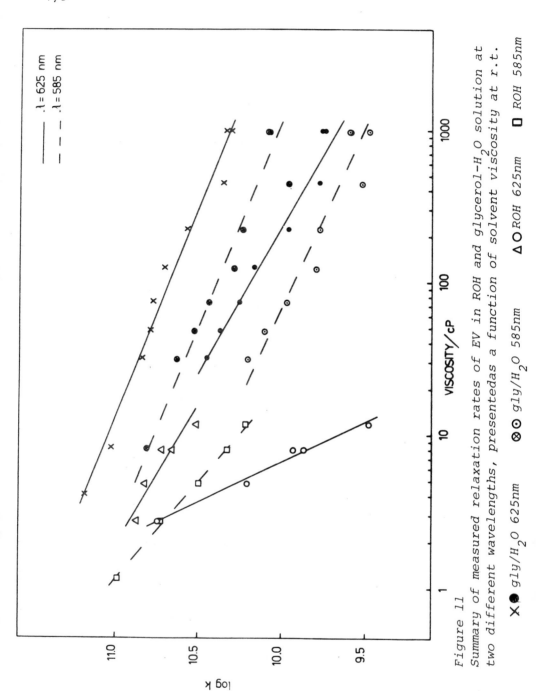

Figure 11

Summary of measured relaxation rates of EV in ROH and glycerol–H_2O solution at two different wavelengths, presented as a function of solvent viscosity at r.t.

it is reasonable to relate the lifetimes measured
in the short-wavelength region of the absorption
spectrum to this structure. This spectral feature
was by Lewis *et al* assigned to a molecular
conformation having a distorted propellar structure[32]
existing in equilibrium with the symmetrical
conformer. τ_1 and τ_2 of CV and EV measured in the
range $550 \leqslant \lambda \leqslant 585$ nm can therefore be associated
with this distorted propellar structure, whereas
the lifetimes for $\lambda \geqslant \lambda_{iso}$ characterize the
symmetrical structure.

iii) The measured lifetimes are strongly viscosity
dependent. The lifetimes are seen to obey the
relation, $\tau = C \cdot \eta^{\alpha}$ with α varying in the range
0.4 - 1.9. We have chosen to present our data in
this way, see figure 11, because the results of
several theoretical considerations are presented
in this manner[15,16,33]. However, it should be
noted that the results could equally well be
fitted to a relation of type, $\tau = \tau_0 + A \cdot \eta$.
Judging from the very large variation in α, it is
quite clear that no one of the theoretical models
currently in use is capable of fully reproducing the
observed viscosity dependencies of relaxation rates.

iv) In time-resolved emission experiments on CV and EV in
n-alcohols[31] only the fast kinetic component (τ_1) can

be detected, suggesting that the lifetime τ_2 is associated with a ground state species.

The various observations on TPM/ROH summarized above can be accounted for by the energy level scheme of figure 12[31]. For the molecules having two ground state conformers (CV, EV, PF) this scheme shows the energy levels for only one conformer; a similar scheme could be constructed for the second conformer. The short lifetime τ_1 is seen to represent the conformation relaxation to a twisted electronic state, S_x which, as indicated by the time-resolved fluorescence measurements mentioned above, most likely is a ground state. Thermal relaxation back to the stable ground state S_0 occurs with lifetime τ_2. The details of this model together with kinetic equations are presented in reference 31.

The appearance of the absorption recovery kinetics and especially the fluorescence kinetics of TPM in glycerol-water solution is quite different from that in n-alcohols. The most important differences are summarized in the following points:

i)   A double exponential fluorescence decay function is observed for CV, EV and MG at all wavelengths. The lifetimes and emission spectra are completely independent of excitation and emission wavelengths. Lifetimes measured in emission agrees very well with the absorption recovery lifetimes (the absorption recovery lifetimes obtained in the red part of the absorption spectrum in the case of CV and EV).

ii) No strongly absorbing species are seen in the absorption measurements.

iii) The viscosity dependence of the measured rate constants in glycerol-water solutions is in general seen to be weaker than in the n-alcohols. The spread in the α-values is also much less, thus, 0.33 < α < 0.54.

If the energy level scheme used for TPM/ROH is modified by increasing the $S_2 - S_x$ energy separation, as shown in figure 13, the observations described above can be explained. This change in the position of the S_2 and S_x levels results in several effects. Firstly, the $S_1 - S_2$ energy gap decreases and a fast equilibrium between these two states is maintained. This is a situation resembling that for p-type delayed fluorescence, and explains the failure to detect any wavelength dependence of the two emission lifetimes and emission spectra. Secondly, the increased $S_2 - S_x$ gap would decrease the rate of this transition and probably make it rate determining. In that case the population of S_x would be low at all times and consequently difficult to detect. The changing level positions will in addition change the positions of the

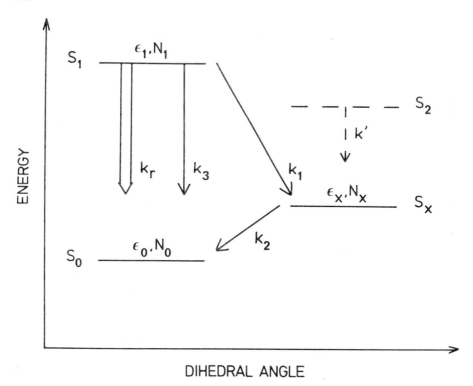

Figure 12   *Model for the TPM photophysics in n-alcohols*

transient absorption bands of these levels. By comparing
the energy level schemes of figures 12 and 13 it is clear
that the rate constant designated k_2, corresponding to the
slower decay of any measured k_1, k_2 pair, does not correspond to the same process in ROH and glycerol-water solutions.
This is also strongly suggested by the viscosity dependence
of k_2, see figure 11. In ROH there is a very strong
dependence, $k_2 \sim n^{-1.9}$ for EV, whereas in glycerol-water
solutions the dependence is considerably weaker,
approximately going as $k_2 \sim n^{-0.5}$. In summary then, the
fast relaxation rate k_1, at any wavelength, is seen to

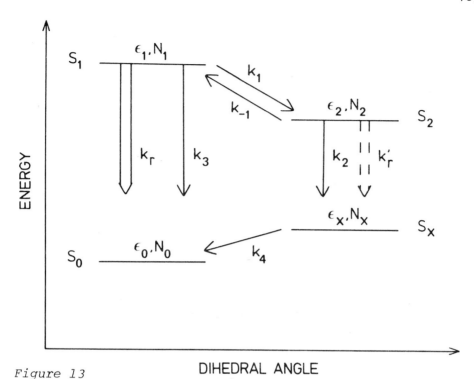

Figure 13

DIHEDRAL ANGLE

Model for the TPM photophysics in glycerol-water solutions.

represent a conformational change in the excited state in
both ROH and glycerol-water solution, to a twisted
electronic state. The somewhat lower viscosity dependence
of k_1 in glycerol-water as compared to ROH can be seen as
a reflection of the influence of micro-viscosity, c.f.
the polymethine dyes. k_2 in ROH solution is seen to
represent a conformational change in the ground state, back
to a stable isomer. The high α value (1.5 - 1.9)
of this process could be compared to that of k_p in the
polymethine dyes (1.0 < α < 1.6). k_p is also seen to
represent a conformational change. In glycerol-water

184

solutions k_2 is seen to represent a 'vertical' process, having a weaker viscosity dependence, more resembling that of k_{ic} of the polymethines. The details of this model and kinetic equations describing the relaxations can be found elsewhere[31].

Acknowledgements

This work was supported by The Swedish Natural Science Research Council.

References

1. B.I. Greene, R.M. Hochstrasser, R.B. Weisman, *J. Chem. Phys*. **70**,(1979) 1247.

2. D.A. Cremers, M.W. Windsor, *Chem. Phys. Lett*. **71**, (1980) 27.

3. S.K. Rentsch, R.V. Danielius, K.A. Gadonas, *Chem. Phys. Lett*. **84**, (1981) 450.

4. D.F. Kelley, P.M. Rentzepis, *Chem.Phys.Lett*. **84**, (1982) 85.

5. V. Sundström, T. Gillbro, *Chem.Phys*. **61**, (1981) 257.

6. D. Waldeck, A.J. Cross, Jr., D.B. McDonald, G.R. Fleming, *J. Chem.Phys*. **74**, (1981) 3381.

7. D.P. Millar, R.J. Robbins, A.H. Zewail, *J. Chem. Phys*. **75**, (1981) 3649.

8. V. Sundström, T.Gillbro, submitted to *Appl.Phys*.

9. E.P.Ippen, C.V. Shank, *Picosecond Phenomena I, eds*. C.V.Shank, E.P. Ippen, S.L. Shapiro (Springer, Berlin, 1978) p.103.

10. J.M. Wiesenfeld, E.P. Ippen, *Chem.Phy.Lett*. **67**, (1979) 213.

11. T. Gillbro, V. Sundström, *Chem.Phys. Lett*. **74**, (1980) 188.

12. V. Sundström, T. Gillbro, submitted to *Chem.Phys.Lett*.

13. J.C. Mialocq, J.Jaraudias, P. Gaujon, *Chem. Phys.Lett*. **47**, (1977) 123.

14. C.J. Tredwell, C.M. Keary, *Chem.Phys*. **43**, (1979) 307.

15. Th. Förster, G. Hoffmann, *Z.Phys. Chem. N.F*. **75**,(1971) 63.

16. G.Osten, Y. Nishijima, *J.Am.Chem.Soc.* **78**,(1956) 1581.

17. V. Sundström, T. Gillbro,*J.Phys.Chem.* **86**, (1982) 1788.

18. D.N. Dempster, T. Morrow, R.Rankin, G.F. Thompson, *J.Chem.Soc., Faraday Trans.2* **68**,(1972) 1479.

19. E.G. Arthurs, D.J. Bradley, A.R.Roddie, *Chem.Phys. Lett.* **22** (1973) 230.

20. J.P. Fouassier, D.-I.Lougnot, J.Faure, *Opt.Commun.* **23** (1977) 393.

21. V.A. Kuzmin, A.P. Darmanyan, *Chem.Phys.Lett.***54** (1978) 159.

22. J.S.McCaskill, R.G.Gilbert, *Chem. Phys.***44** (1979) 389.

23. R.M. Hochstrasser, *Pure Appl.Chem.* **52**, (1980) 2683.

24. S.P. Velsko, G.R. Fleming, *Chem.Phys.* **65**,(1982) 59.

25. S.P. Velsko, G.R. Fleming, *J. Chem.Phys.* **76**, (1982) 3553.

26. T.J. Chuang, K.B. Eisenthal, *Chem.Phys.Lett.* **11** (1971) 368.

27. S.A.Rice, G.A. Kenney-Wallace, *Chem.Phys.***47**, (1980) 161.

28. D. Magde, M.W. Windsor,*Chem.Phys.Lett.* **24**,(1974) 144.

29. E.P. Ippen, C.V. Shank, A. Bergman, *Chem.Phys.Lett.* **38**, (1976) 611.

30. M.D. Hirsch, H. Mahr, *Chem.Phys.Lett.* **60** (1979) 299.

31. V.Sundström, T.Gillbro, *Chem.Phys.* (1982).

32. G.N. Lewis, T.T. Magel, B. Lipkin, *J.Am.Chem.Soc.* 64, (1942) 1774.

33. B. Wilhelmi, *Chem. Phys.* 66, (1982) 351.

The Synchronously Mode-Locked $F_A(II)$ KCl:Li Colour Centre Laser

L. Reekie, I.S. Ruddock and R. Illingworth

Department of Natural Philosophy, University of Strathclyde, 107 Rottenrow, Glasgow G4 0NG, UK.

Abstract

A study of the synchronously mode-locked $F_A(II)$ colour centre laser ($\lambda = 2.7\mu m$) is presented. Results discussed include the cavity length detuning characteristics and coherence measurements of the system for argon-ion laser pumping.

Introduction

In the past few years interest has been shown in the synchronously mode-locked colour centre laser as a source of tunable picosecond pulses in the near infrared region of the spectrum. To date, the krypton-ion laser pumped $LiF:F_2^+$ colour centre laser[1], tunable over the range 0.82 - 1.07μm and the Nd:YAG pumped $KF:F_2^+$ laser[2], tunable between 1.24 and 1.45μm, have been successfully mode-locked. The $LiF:F_2^+$ colour centre laser has also been mode-locked using the frequency doubled Nd:YAG laser as a pump source[3] while more recently mode-locked operation of the thallium doped KCl crystal has been reported[4].

Although capable of high average output powers and good quantum efficiency, sustained pumping of the F_2^+ colour centre crystals causes bleaching of the centres which reduces the output power and limits the usefulness of the laser. The $F_A(II)$ type centre, in which lasing was first observed in colour centres[5], does not suffer from this effect. In addition, the tuning range of $F_A(II)$ type centres lies in the 2-3µm region of the spectrum, within the excitation range of several important molecular vibrational levels. A preliminary attempt to mode-lock the $F_A(II)$ colour centre laser using a lithium doped KCℓ crystal[6] achieved typical pulse durations of 75ps, an order of magnitude larger than is possible with the F_2^+ colour centre laser. In this paper a study of the detuning characteristics of the mode-locked KCℓ:Li $F_A(II)$ colour centre laser is presented.

Experimental

A modified Burleigh FCL-10 colour centre laser was pumped by an acousto-optically mode-locked Spectra Physics 165 argon-ion (Ar^+) laser. The Ar^+ laser produced pulses of ∿150ps duration at $\lambda = 514.5$ nm and at a pulse repetition rate of 138 MHz. The modification to the colour centre laser consisted of replacing the tuning arm supplied with an evacuated extended cavity. The vacuum was maintained at 10^{-3} Torr and a liquid N_2 cold trap was added to eliminate intracavity water absorption. The cavity was a conventional 3-mirror folded astigmatically compensated design, with a coated intracavity CaF_2 beamsplitter being used to couple the Ar^+ pump beam into the crystal. The beamsplitter coating was optimised for a krypton-ion pump laser and so the coupling efficiency was only ~50% for λ = 514.5nm. The crystal chamber was also maintained at ~10^{-3} Torr separate from the external cavity and the crystal was mounted on a cold finger below a cryostat enabling laser operation at liquid N_2 temperature (77°K). A double bellows arrangement around the output coupler allowed the evacuated cavity length to be altered by a few mm in order to study the cavity length detuning characteristics when mode-locked. In our case the colour centre laser cavity length was made equal to that of the Ar^+ laser (L = 1.09m) in contrast to Reference 6 where the cavity length was chosen to be one quarter that of the pump laser. A high reflectivity output coupler was used (R $\simeq$ 99%) with no intracavity tuning element. Lasing occurred near the gain peak at $\lambda \simeq 2.7\mu m$.

Results

Output power measurements show that the slope efficiency of the laser when mode-locked is similar to that of the cw laser although the average threshold power is about 20mW less. This is not as significant as in the mode-locked dye laser where the average threshold power may be 2 to 3 times less than that for cw operation. The slope efficiency can be seen to fall off sharply towards the shorter cavity lengths (Figure 1). $\Delta L = 0$ has been chosen as that

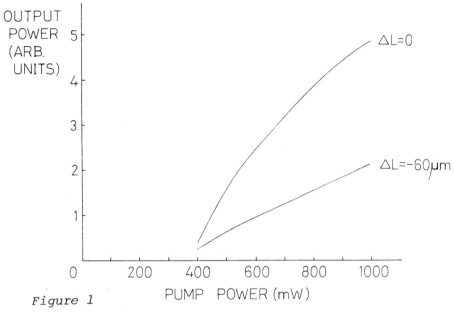

Figure 1

PUMP POWER (mW)

*Slope efficiency curves for mode-locked colour centre
laser at* $\Delta L = O$ *and* $\Delta L = - 60\mu m$.

position which gives lowest average threshold power when
mode-locked. There is a noticeable roll-off in output
power as the pump power is increased with both cw and
mode-locked operation. This is probably caused by thermal
effects in the crystal due to the large Stokes shift
between absorption and emission.

Figure 2 shows a typical cavity length detuning
characteristic for the mode-locked colour centre laser
near threshold (pump power = 440 mW). The colour centre
laser output for the same average pump power, but with the
mode-locker switched off, is shown as a reference. For
cavity lengths shorter than that of the matched position

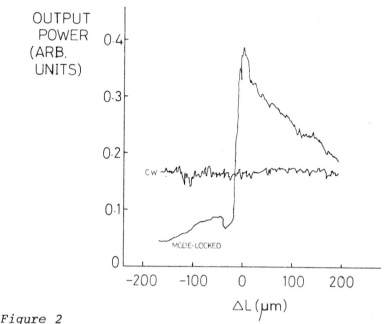

Figure 2
    Cavity length detuning characteristic of mode-locked colour centre laser near threshold (pump power = 440mW).

(ΔL-ve) the mode-locked output is less than that of the cw laser output. This is to be expected since at short cavity lengths the intracavity pulse will arrive at the crystal early with respect to the pump pulse and will therefore only experience gain due to the leading edge of this pulse. In this regime the mode-locked laser would perhaps give two pulses instead of one as the gain medium recovers above threshold after passage of the first pulse. Increasing the cavity length causes the power to increase above the cw power level, eventually falling off as the detuning becomes too severe to sustain proper mode-locking. In this respect the behaviour is similar to that of the

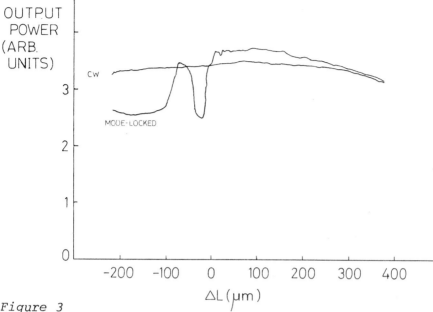

Figure 3
   Cavity length detuning characteristic well above
threshold (pump power = 800mW).

synchronously mode-locked cw dye laser. Figure 3 shows

the results obtained at higher pump power (pump power

= 800 mW). In this case the peak in the output power is not

as prominent as it was near threshold and also a significant

drop in the power has appeared at $\Delta L \simeq -20\mu m$. The reason for

this power loss is currently under investigation.

As a preliminary to determining the pulse duration the

coherence length of the pulses was measured with a Michelson

interferometer. A short coherence length demonstrates the

possibility of generating short pulses as the synchronously

pumped gain medium would be capable of responding to at least

picosecond noise structure. A fast scan of the coherence

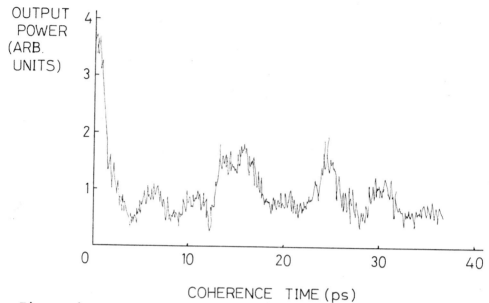

Figure 4

Coherence trace of mode-locked colour centre laser at
ΔL = +20µm.

length was obtained by rectifying the output of the PbS
detector used so that the drift in the cavity length was
minimised. For cavity lengths other than optimum, the
coherence trace consists of a large central feature of width
~ 2.5ps fWHM with several irregular features in the wings
(figure 4). A contributory factor to this effect may be
residual water absorption in the atmosphere external to the
laser cavity. At ΔL = 0 (figure 5) the central feature
broadens and the irregularities in the wings disappear, being
replaced by a low level constant background. Such a narrow
coherence time, indicative of good mode-locking, only appears
within a cavity detuning of < ± 5µm from the optimum.

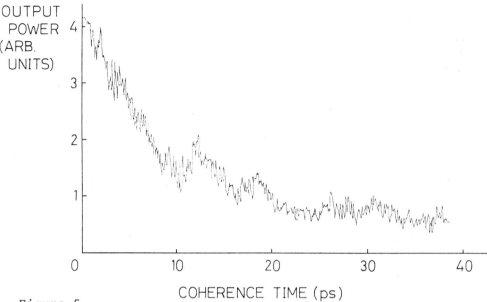

Figure 5

Coherence trace of mode-locked colour centre laser at $\Delta L = 0$.

Conclusions

We have presented cavity detuning and coherence measurements for a synchronously pumped F_A(II) KCℓ:Li cw colour centre laser. The results are consistent with mode-locking behaviour and the short coherence time of a few picoseconds shows that the system is capable of responding to and supporting pulses of a similar duration. Also recent experiments[4] demonstrating successful mode-locking of a colour centre laser with long fluorescence decay time suggest that the 75 ns decay time of the F_A(II) centre should not pose any problem. Further work will involve non-linear pulse measurements, picosecond excitation and an investigation of synchronous mode-locking of longer wavelength colour centres.

References

1. L.F. Mollenauer, D. M. Bloom, A.M. Del Gaudio, *Opt. Lett.* **3**, 48 (1978).

2. L.F. Mollenauer, D. M. Bloom, *Opt.Lett.* **4**,247 (1979).

3. T.T. Basiev, N.S. Vorob'ev, S.B. Mirov, V.V. Osiko, P.P. Pashinin, V.E. Postovalov, A.M. Prokhorov, *JETP Lett.* **31**, 316 (1980).

4. L.F. Mollenauer, N.D. Vieira, L. Szeto, *Opt.Lett.* **7**, 414 (1982).

5. B. Fritz, E. Menke, *Solid State Comm.* **3**, 61 (1965).

6. L.Isganitis, M.G Sceats,K.R. German, *Opt.Lett.* **5**, 7 (1979).

Application of Synchronously Scanning Streak Cameras to Picosecond Time Resolved Luminescence Measurements

W. Sibbett, W.E. Sleat and J.R. Taylor

*Laser Optics Section, Physics Department,
Imperial College, Prince Consort Road, London SW7 2BZ*

Abstract

The operation and pertinent characteristics of the current synchroscan streak camera are described and its application to the study of the fluorescence recovery of saturable absorbing species is given. Particular emphasis is given to the examination of the viscosity dependent recovery time and inter-molecular dipole-dipole energy transfer and how these mechanisms may be applied to modifying the aperture time and hence the necessary saturation flux of saturable absorbing species.

Introduction

Single-shot streak cameras have been extensively used in conjunction with pulsed lasers in the examination of luminous events on a picosecond time scale[1-7] and although these devices have exhibited picosecond[8] and subpicosecond[9] resolution, they are not particularly well suited to applications with c.w. mode-locked lasers, where sub picosecond pulses can now be generated quite routinely with

passive[10], synchronous[11] and hybrid[12] mode-locking
techniques. As early as 1972 it was realised[13] that
utilizing the repetitive output of a c.w. mode-locked
laser system to generate and be in synchronism with a
sequence of streaking ramps, picosecond resolution could
be maintained while increasing the information gathering
rate, improving the signal to noise ratio and increasing
the dynamic range of the camera compared to the single
linear voltage ramp system. The integrating nature of the
recording means that very weak intensity luminous events
can be recorded with low excitation power densities.

In this paper a brief introduction to the principle of
operation of the synchroscan streak camera system is
followed by representative results of its application to
the study of saturable absorbing species throughout the
visible spectrum where the detection of low quantum
efficiency fluorescence emission is of primary importance.

Principle of Operation

Operation of the streak camera in a continuous mode is most
conveniently produced by the application of a high
frequency ($\sim$100 MHz) sinusoidal voltage to the deflection
plates of a standard Photochron streak tube. The
principle of operation is shown schematically in figure 1
and a typical experimental arrangement used to generate
the voltage sinusoid and to register the resulting

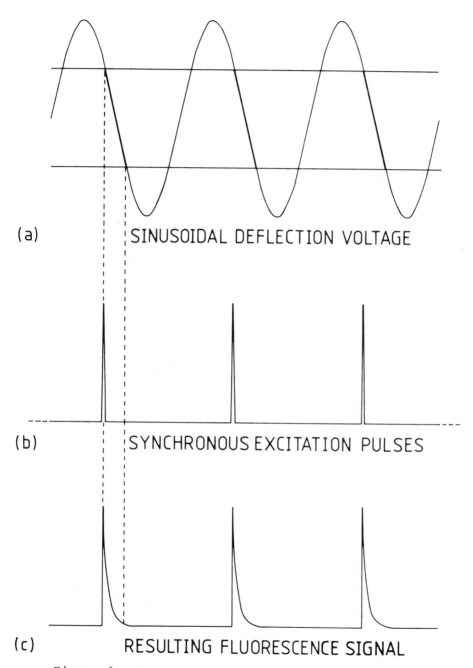

(a) SINUSOIDAL DEFLECTION VOLTAGE

(b) SYNCHRONOUS EXCITATION PULSES

(c) RESULTING FLUORESCENCE SIGNAL

Figure 1   Synchroscan principle of operation

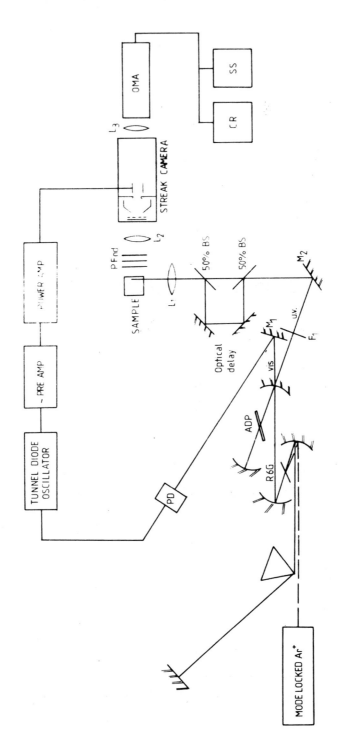

Figure 2   Typical experimental arrangement

luminescence is shown in figure 2. In pulsed operation, the
application of a linear voltage ramp (∿1.5 Kv) on the
deflection plates is arranged such that the time evolving
electron image of the luminous event which was incident on
the photocathode is swept across the phosphor where it can be
recorded. In synchroscan mode[14], a continuous sinusoid with
a typical peak to peak amplitude of ∿3.5 kv is derived from
a fraction of and in synchronism with the periodic output of
a c.w. mode-locked laser. The central portion of the driving
signal (the amplified output from the tunnel diode) which is
approximately half the amplitude of the sine wave deviates
from linearity by less than 5% and thus only this portion of
the waveform is used for streak purposes (see figure 1a).
The remainder of the laser output is used to excite the
photoluminescent sample such that the fluorescent output
also occurs at the driving frequency of the mode-locked
laser (see figures 1b and c). By varying optical or
electrical delays, it is easily arranged that the
fluorescence signal arrives at the image tube such that it
experiences a periodic linear deflection. The phase is such
that the luminous event under investigation arrives at the
beginning of the linear ramp and develops during it (figures
1a and c).

The linear half amplitude of a sinusoid lasts for
approximately one sixth of the period, which means that at
a laser repetition rate of 140 MHz, the useful linear window
of the camera is 1.2 ns. By varying the amplitude of the

driving signal, the streak speed and the effective
recording window together with the time resolution can
be varied. The repetition rate of the light emitting
event may be a sub-multiple or higher harmonic of the
camera frequency, but in the latter case, care must be
taken in the interpretation of the recorded images, since
the time axis of the streak is reversed after each half
cycle. It can also be seen from figure 1 that the duration
of any fluorescent signal at the fundamental repetition
rate must not temporally exceed the period of the sinusoid
nor even that of the linear window, although the latter
problem has now been overcome.

The net effect of the synchronous sweeping is that
successive identical sweep records are precisely
superimposed on the image tube phosphor at rates the order
of 100 MHz, while integrated time resolution as low as 1 ps
is maintained. Since information is accumulated at 10^8
sec $^{-1}$, the detection of low intensity events is enhanced
and in most cases no further image intensification is
required. The recorded images are then readily displayed
using optical multichannel analysers or stored and
transferred for computation.

Temporal Resolution of the Synchroscan System

To determine the temporal resolution of the streak camera
in the synchroscan mode of operation, the mode-locked dye

laser was used as the source of repetitive, reproducible, ultrashort, frequency tunable pulses. The best source being the passively mode-locked ring dye laser[10] which consistently give pulses of <200 fs[15] as measured by auto-correlation methods. These pulses incident on a Photochron IIA[16] synchroscan streak camera gave recorded pulse durations of 1.2 ps (see figure 3b). Allowing for the technical and instrumental temporal resolutions of 0.8 and 0.9 ps respectively, this result demonstrated that the actual pulse width and the long term temporal jitter of the camera system were both subpicosecond.

However, when used in conjunction with a synchronously mode-locked dye laser for which autocorrelation traces indicated that the actual pulse widths were $\sim$0.5 ps[12] with an identical electronic system to that used above, the shortest recorded synchroscan streak images are 6.5 - 7 ps (see figure 3a). This loss of resolution can be explained by the differences in the methods of pulse generation in the passive and synchronous mode-locked dye laser systems. In the former, effective pulse generation occurs principally from a noise signal saturating the saturable absorber and subsequent stages of saturable absorption and saturable amplification of the noise burst lead to the pulse formation. In the synchronously pumped mode-locked dye laser, pulse formation occurs at the active medium and within the relatively wide temporal gain window provided by the pumping mode-locked pulse from the Ar ion laser ($\geq$ 60 ps[17]. It can be seen that in the long term pulse buildup in

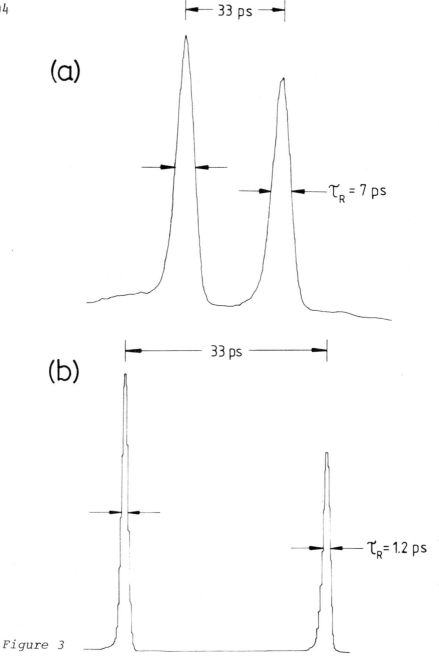

(a)

33 ps

$\tau_R = 7$ ps

(b)

33 ps

$\tau_R = 1.2$ ps

Figure 3

Synchroscan streak camera resolution measurements of subpicosecond pulses from (a) synchronous and (b) passively mode-locked dye lasers.

subsequent round trips from noise preceeding the main pulse can occur which will give rise to an effective movement of the dye laser pulse in time. This in turn manifests itself as a broadened image when recorded on the synchroscan streak camera over a period of $\sim$1 sec[17]. Improved resolution should be obtained by using much shorter pump pulses or with the inclusion of a saturable absorber in a hybrid arrangement.

Time Resolved Emission from Species with Low Quantum Efficiency

A distinct advantage of the synchronously operated streak camera is that streak information is accumulated and precisely superimposed at rates of $10^8 s^{-1}$ which enhances the detection of low intensity events. In pulsed systems, the irradiation power densities needed to adequately record a low intensity fluorescence profile in a single shot can give rise to non-linear effects in the sample which consequently modify the recorded lifetime[18,19]. The advantage of the synchroscan camera system in the detection of emission from species with low quantum yields can be seen in the case of phthalazine (2,3-diazanaphthalene). This molecule which exhibits no detectable fluorescence emission using conventional excitation techniques, has a fluorescence lifetime estimated to be in the picosecond regime with a quantum efficiency $<10^{-3}$. The experimental arrangement was similar to that in figure 2. A frequency doubled synchronously pumped c.w. dye laser provided the source of excitation pulses. This laser system which has

been described previously[20] with the inclusion of an
intracavity 1.5mm thick ADP crystal typically produced pulses
of ∿2ps in duration at a 70 MHz repetition rate and was
tunable in the U.V. from 285-308 nm. The average power in
the beam after passing through the filter F, to remove any
visible radiation was at maximum 1mW (peak power per pulse
∿7W). This U.V. output was directed via mirror M_2 through
an optical delay line which provided a calibration mechanism
and a linearity check for the streak camera. For the
fluorescence decay measurements, only one beam was used.
Lens L_2 was used to focus the excitation pulses (λ = 304 nm)
into the 10 mm square cross section quartz cell containing
the sample. A maximum excitation power density of ∿3 Kw
cm^{-2} was used. The fluorescence which was detected at
right angles with respect to the incident beam was passed
through a polarizer P set at 54.7° to the incident
polarization to remove any distortion due to fluorescence
depolarization[21] and then through a filter F to select the
waveband of interest, n.d. filters (if necessary), before
being focussed using lens L_2 on to the input slit of the
streak camera.

Derivation of the streak deflection voltage was achieved
by directing the visible light which leaked through the
nominally 100% reflecting laser cavity mirror on to a photodiode. The generated electrical signal triggered a tunnel
diode oscillator in synchronism with the driving pulses.
After amplification up to powers of ∿15W, this sinusoidal

voltage ramp was applied to the streak plates. Synchronism was achieved as described in the previous section.

The recrystalized phthalazine (Aldrich Chem.) was dissolved as a 5×10^{-4}M solution in spectroscopic grade 1,2-dichloroethane. Figure 4 shows a typical time resolved fluorescence profile recorded by the system (a calibration step of 100 ps is indicated). With pure solvent only in the cell and the camera sensitivity at a maximum, no detectable fluorescence decay was observed, indicating that the emission arose from the phthalazine. From previous measurements of the maximum absorption cross section of phthalazine[22] at room temperature the natural radiative lifetime has been estimated to be 1.7×10^{-6}s hence from the recorded fluorescence lifetime of 181 ps, the fluorescence quantum yield ϕ_F can be estimated to be 1.1×10^{-4}. This clearly illustrates the sensitivity and ability of the synchroscan streak camera system to detect the weak luminescent emission arising from low excitation powers.

Viscosity Dependent Recovery Time of Saturable Absorbers
Although the passively mode-locked ring dye laser produces the shortest pulses directly obtainable from a laser, passive mode-locking of c.w. dye lasers for the production of subpicosecond pulses has been essentially restricted

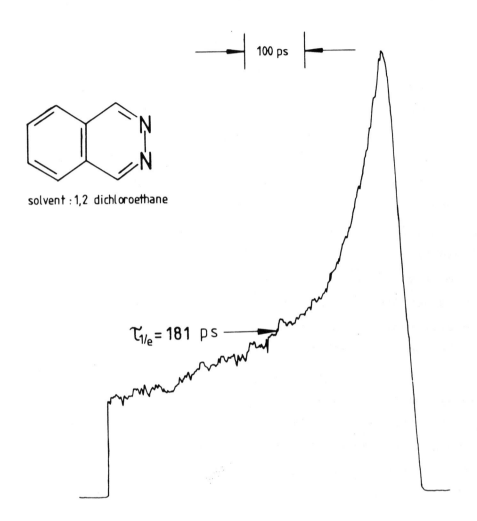

solvent : 1,2 dichloroethane

100 ps

$\tau_{1/e} = 181$ ps

Figure 4

    Fluorescence decay profile of phthalazine (5 x 10^{-4}M in dichloroethane Φ F $\simeq$ 10^{-4}).

to the rhodamine 6G/DODCI combination, frequency tunable
around 615 nm. Although the prerequisite features of a
saturable absorber for passive mode-locking dye lasers are
rather modest[23], until recently only a small range of
wavelengths have been covered. It is now possible by the
selection of suitable saturable absorbers and appropriate
tailoring of their saturation parameters to obtain passive
mode-locking through much of the visible range[24].

If one examines the typical flux F_{sat} needed to saturate
for example the dye DODCI, ($F_{sat} = (\sigma\tau)^{-1}$ where σ is the
absorption cross section and τ the absorber recovery time,
at 605 nm $\sigma = 1 \times 10^{-16}$ cm^2 and $\tau = 1.2$ ns) then a power
density of 2.75 MW cm^{-2} is required which can easily be
obtained in a flashlamp pumped dye laser or at the focus of
a folded mirror section in a c.w. dye laser. In the green
and blue regions where laser efficiencies are lower reduction
of the required saturation flux can be accomplished through
a modification of the absorber's recovery time rather than
in the absorption cross section. The structure and
absorption profiles of several saturable absorbing species
potentially capable of mode-locking over the range 400 nm -
600 nm are shown in figures 5 and 6 respectively. These are
2 AVBOMI [2-ω-anilinovinlybenzoxazolyl methyl iodide], DASPI
[2-(p-dimethylaminostryryl)-pyridylmethyl iodide], 4 AVQEI
[4-ω-anilinovinyl quinolylethyl iodide] and DASBTI [2-(p-
dimethylamino styryl)-benzothiazolylethyl iodide with peak
absorptions in ethanol at 380 nm, 459 nm, 483 nm and 524 nm,
and maximum extinction coefficients of 2.2, 1.8, 2.7 and 3 x

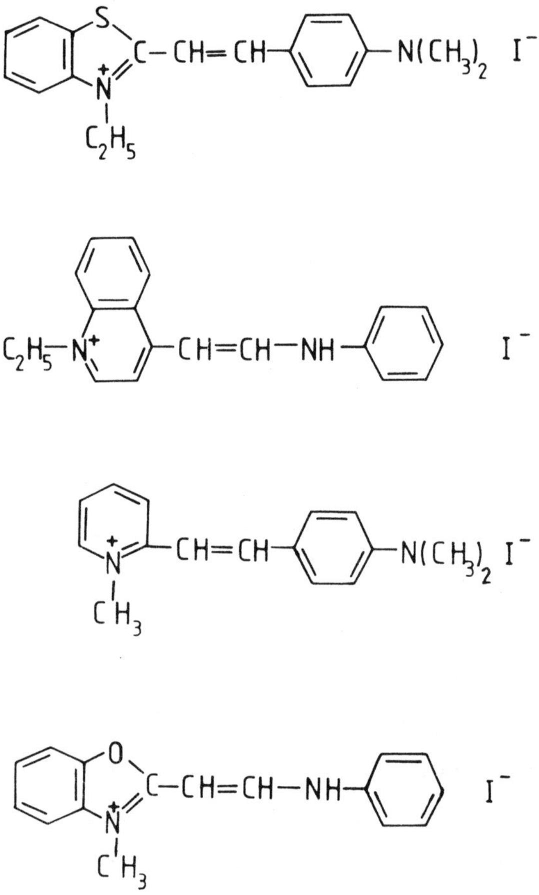

DASBTI

4ωAVQEI

DASPI

2ωAVBOMI

Figure 5

Structure of saturable absorbing dyes for the 400nm - 600nm spectral region, see text for nomenclature.

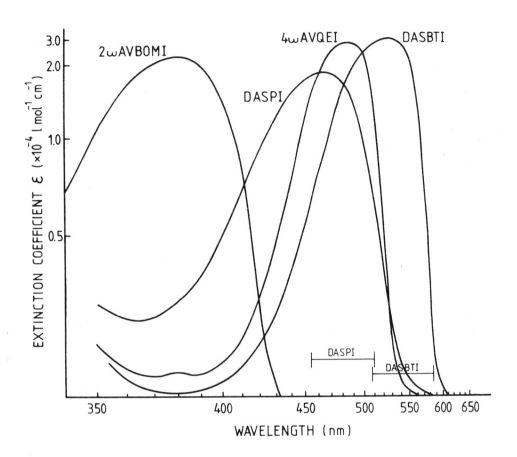

Figure 6

Absorption profile in ethanol of dyes in figure 5.

10^4 l mol^{-1} cm^{-1} ($\sigma = 3.84 \times 10^{-21} \, \varepsilon$) respectively.
Effective dissipation of excitation energy within these
dyes occurs through partial rotation of the aromatic
terminal groups about the linking aliphatic chain.
Consequently the rate of internal conversion, which has
been shown to be a dominant mechanism in the relaxation
process of these dyes, should show a strong dependence on
processes which tend to limit the twisting action. It
was generally shown that the rate of internal conversation
was reduced in viscous solvents through a restriction of
this rotational motion with a consequential increase in
the fluorescence quantum efficiency and hence fluorescence
lifetime[25,26]. For the triphenylmethanes it has been
shown that $\tau \alpha \eta^{2/3}$ where τ is the fluorescence lifetime
and η the solvent viscosity and similar relationships have
been seen to occur in several merocyanine[27] and polymethine[20]
dyes. Recently Wilhelmi[32] has introduced a good kinetic
model taking account of internal rotation and internal
conversion predicting fluorescence decays of the form
$\tau = A\eta^{\alpha}$ where α is a parameter depending on the molecule,
and this theoretical model agrees closely with experimental
results[20].

The experimental arrangement used to examine the
viscosity dependence was similar to that shown in figure
2 where either the fundamental or second harmonic
frequency was used as the excitation source depending
on the absorption profile of the dye of interest.
Keeping the temperature constant, the viscosity of the

solution was varied by mixing known proportions of ethanol and glycerol. To ensure homogeneity, the solvent mixture was placed in a vibration bath some time before use. Typical fluorescence decays are shown in figure 7 for DASPI (excitation at 580 nm) where the measured lifetime was seen to increase from 62 ps at 1.1 cp to 306 ps at 60 cp. Similar results were obtained for the other dyes in figure 5 and these are shown in figure 8. For clarity the results for DASBTI which had a fluorescence lifetime of 58 ps at 1 cp and closely paralleled the trend of DASPI have been omitted. Over the range of viscosity examined, the fluorescence lifetime of DASPI showed an increase (and hence a corresponding decrease in its saturation flux) of approximately one order of magnitude. For lower viscosities, the relationship between τ and η approximately followed the relationship $\tau = K\eta^{2/3}$ (a gradient of 2/3 is drawn through the lower data points for DASPI and 4 AVQEI in figure 8) before tending to level out. For 2 AVBOMI the much reduced gradient (= 0.36) is an indication of a greater rate of internal conversion compared to that of 4 AVQEI[32].

From these examples, it can be seen that the saturation parameters of many saturable absorbing dyes can be manipulated to achieve ease of saturation and hence laser mode-locking. Using viscous solutions of absorbers, mode-locking has been achieved in a variety of coumarin and xanthene dyes throughout the visible using polymethines[28] and the dyes above. Picosecond pulse generation has been achieved from 455 nm - 585 nm using either DASPI or DASBTI

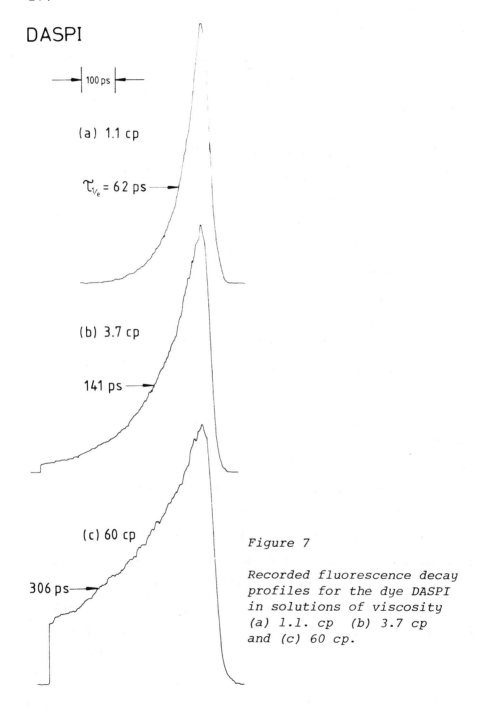

DASPI

100 ps

(a) 1.1 cp

$\tau_{1/e}$ = 62 ps

(b) 3.7 cp

141 ps

(c) 60 cp

306 ps

Figure 7

Recorded fluorescence decay profiles for the dye DASPI in solutions of viscosity (a) 1.1. cp (b) 3.7 cp and (c) 60 cp.

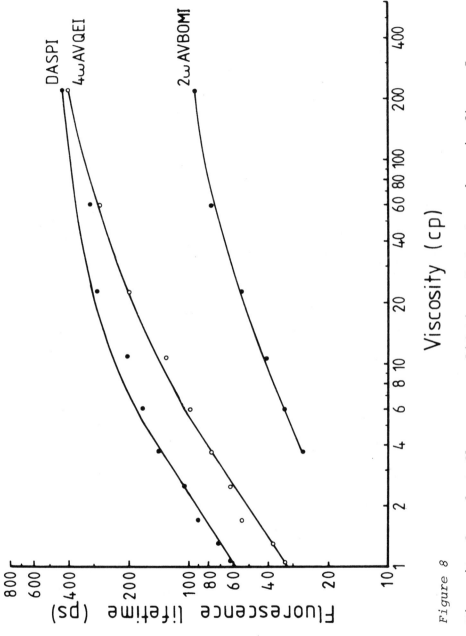

Figure 8

Viscosity dependent fluorescence lifetime of the dyes shown in figure 5.

and the mode-locking range of each is shown in figure 6.
Potentially 2 AVBOMI which has similar characteristics,
could be used in the blue/uv region and work on this is
in progress.

Energy Transfer Between Saturable Absorbers

For some applications rather than increasing the aperture
time of the saturable absorber, it is necessary to reduce
it. This is the case when they have extra cavity uses
such as isolation stages for picosecond pulses or for
pulse shaping. In such an instance, the leading edge of
a pulse to be shortened is removed by the absorber which
then transmits for the short period of its lifetime
before rapidly returning to its ground state, at which
time the restored absorption is responsible for the
removal of the rear of the incident pulse and hence pulse
shortening results. One method of reducing the upper
state lifetime of a species is through resonant energy
transfer via dipole-dipole interaction. Originally
considered theoretically by Förster[29], the rate at which
energy is transferred from donor D to acceptor A is

$$K_{D*A} = \frac{1}{\tau}\left(\frac{Ro}{R}\right)^6$$

where τ is the fluorescence lifetime in the absence of
energy transfer and R the intermolecular distance. The
critical transfer distance R_o is the distance at which
non radiative dipole-dipole energy transfer has the same
probability as the sum of all other de-excitation

processes of the donor excited state and is given by

$$R_O^6 = \frac{9000 \; \ell n 10 \; \phi_D \; K^2}{128 \; \pi^5 \; \eta^4 \; N} \int_O^\infty \frac{F_D(\nu) \; \varepsilon_A(\nu)}{\nu^4} \; d\nu$$

where η is the refractive index, N is Avagadro's number, $F_D(\nu)$ the donor fluorescence profile and $\varepsilon_A(\nu)$ the acceptors absorption profile. It can be seen that the rate of transfer is enhanced where the fluorescence efficiency of the donor ϕ_D is large and also if the donor fluorescence profile and acceptor absorption profile overlap considerably. K^2 is a molecular orientation factor which has a value of 2/3 for a random directional distribution.

In the presence of energy transfer, the normal fluorescence decay

$$I_F(t) = I_F(o) \; \exp(-t/\tau)$$

is modified to

$$I_O(t) = I_D(o) \; \exp(-t/\tau) [\exp -2\gamma(t/\tau)^{\frac{1}{2}}]$$

where $\gamma = C_A/C_A^O$ and C_A is the acceptor concentration while C_A^O is the critical concentration which has a value $3000/2\pi^{3/2} NR_O^3$. It can be seen that a plot of $\log[I_D(t)/I_F(t)]$ vs $t^{\frac{1}{2}}$ should give a linear dependence of gradient $[-2\gamma/2.303 \; \tau^{\frac{1}{2}}]$ from which the critical transfer distance R_O should be obtained.

The fluorescence of the common saturable absorber for 600 nm, DODCI, considerably overlaps the absorption profile of malachite green and the combination has frequently been used as a saturable absorber mixture. Detection of the DODCI (donor) fluorescence was with a system similar to that in figure 2 without the harmonic generation section and the signal was passed through a narrow band monochromator to eliminate fluorescence from the malachite green (although this is low $\phi_F \simeq 10^{-4}$). Low peak power excitation was used ($\sim 300W$) and all other components were as in figure 2.

A reduction in the recorded fluorescence lifetime (see figure 9) of a $10^{-4}M$ ethanolic solution of DODCI of 1150 ps ± 40 ps was seen to occur on increasing the malachite green (M.G.) concentration to 1060 ps (10^{-5}_M M.G.), 961 ps ($10^{-4}M$), 751 ps ($10^{-3}M$), 510 ps ($2.5 \times 10^{-3}M$) and 260 ps ($7.5 \times 10^{-3}M$). The decrease was most evident where the acceptor concentration was greater than the donor concentration.

Figure 9 ▶

Fluorescence decay curves of a 10^{-4} M ethanolic solution of DODCI plus (a) 0, (b) $10^{-5}M$ (c) $10^{-4}M$ (d) $10^{-3}M$ (e) $2.5 \times 10^{-3}M$ and (f) $7.5 \times 10^{-3}M$ malachite green. The time calibration being constant throughout.

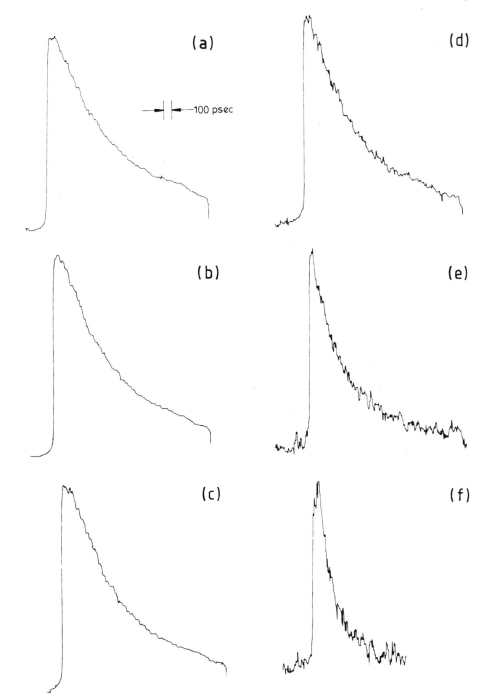

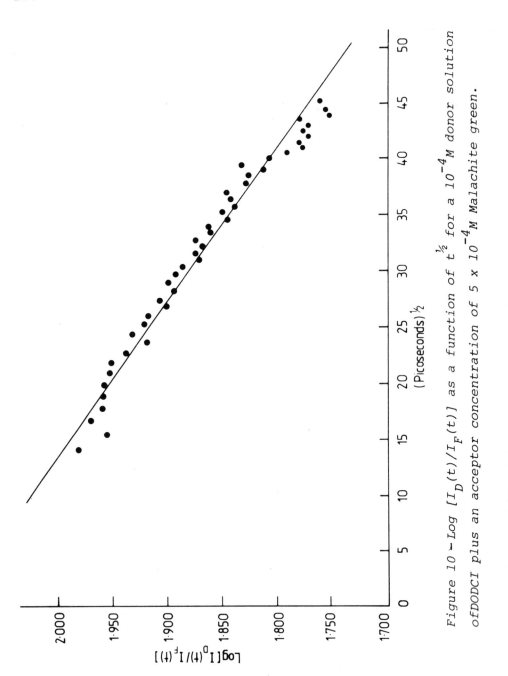

Figure 10 – Log $[I_D(t)/I_F(t)]$ as a function of $t^{1/2}$ for a 10^{-4} M donor solution of DODCI plus an acceptor concentration of 5×10^{-4} M Malachite green.

An average value of the critical transfer distance R_o was obtained from computation of the modified profiles as described above, and from, for example, the data from Figure 10. At high concentrations of the acceptor, the value of R_o approached an average value of $\sim 45\overset{o}{A}$[30]. However, at low acceptor concentrations the Förster formalism inferred much larger values ($\overset{>}{\sim}100\overset{o}{A}$) of R_o and as can be seen from figure 11b the theoretically modified fluorescence decay profile does not correspond particularly well with the experimental result. On the other hand, for high acceptor concentrations, the agreement is quite good (figure 11a). This failure at low acceptor concentrations can be explained by considering that in this circumstance R is large, and consequently the energy transfer rate varying as R^{-6} becomes small and the decay of the donor excited state population is not well described by the Förster modifying term $(2\gamma(t/\tau)^{\frac{1}{2}})$.

The convenience of the real time capability of the synchroscan streak camera for measurements of this type in which data is obtained for weakly emitting species under low power excitation, makes it a powerful tool in picosecond luminescence studies. Using new read out techniques[31] it should be possible to increase the time window of the synchroscan streak camera while maintaining picosecond resolution and Table 1 summarises the characteristics of the currently operational system.

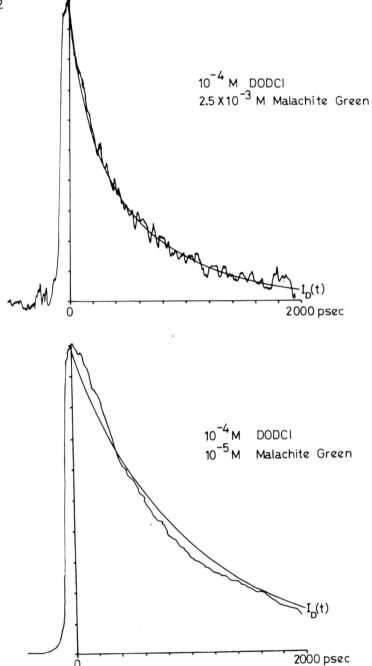

10^{-4} M DODCI
2.5×10^{-3} M Malachite Green

$I_D(t)$

2000 psec

10^{-4} M DODCI
10^{-5} M Malachite Green

$I_D(t)$

2000 psec

Table 1

Characteristics of the Synchroscan streak camera

Driving source	Mode locked laser
	c.w. cavity dumped
	q - switched mode-locked
	Synchroton
Spectral range	vuv - ir
Temporal resolution	<1ps
Upper time window	~20 ns (at 25MHz)
Dynamic range	10^3 - 10^4 limited by read out system
Sensitivity	ϕ_f > 10^{-4}

Acknowledgements

The contributions to the work described here by former*
and present colleagues in the picosecond laser group at
Imperial College is gratefully acknowledged; in particular
Dr M.C. Adams*, Dr J.P. Willson*, Mr P.G. May and Mr K Smith.
The overall financial support for the work was
provided by the SERC.

◀ *Figure 11*

*Experimental and computer plots assuming Förster
kinetics of the time dependent donor fluorescence decay
of a 10^{-4}M DODCI solution with (a) 2.5 x 10^{-3}M and (b)
10^{-5}M Malachite green.*

References

1. E.G. Arthurs, D.J. Bradley, and A.G. Roddie, *Chem. Phys.Lett.***22** 230 (1973).

2. S.L. Shapiro, A.J. Campillo, V.H. Kollman and W.B. Goad, *Opt.Commun.,* 15, 308 (1975).

3. G.S. Beddard, G. Porter and C.J. Tredwell, *Nature* **258**, 116, (1975).

4. G.R. Fleming, A.W.E. Knight, J.M. Morris, R.J. S. Morrison and G.W.Robinson, *J.Am.Chem.Soc.,* **99** 4306 (1977).

5. S.F. Bryant, V.S. Dneprovskii and W. Sibbett, *Appl.Phys.Lett.,* **33**,863, (1978).

6. M. Stavola, G. Mourou and W. Knox, *Opt.Commun.,* **34** 404 (1980).

7. F. Pellegrino, A.Dagen and R.R. Alfano, *Chem.Phys.,* **67**, 111 (1982).

8. D.J. Bradley, B. Liddy and W.E. Sleat, *Opt. Commun.,* **2**, 391 (1971).

9. R.S. Adrain, E.G. Arthurs and W. Sibbett, *Opt. Commun.,* **15**, 290 (1975).

10. R.L. Fork, B.I. Greene and C.V. Shank, *Appl.Phys.Lett.,* **38**, 671 (1981).

11. G.A. Mourou and T. Sizer, *Opt. Commun.,* **41**,47 (1982).

12. P.G. May, W. Sibbett and J.R.Taylor, *Appl. Phys.,* **26B**, 179 (1981).

13. W. Sibbett, *Ph.D. Thesis,* Queen's University, Belfast, (1973).

14. M.C. Adams, W. Sibbett and D.J. Bradley, *Opt.Commun.,* **26**, 273 (1978).

15. J.P. Willson, W. Sibbett and W.E. Sleat, *Opt.Commun.*, **42**, 208 (1982).

16. W. Sibbett, W.E. Sleat, J.R. Taylor and J.P.Willson, *Proc.XV International Congress on High Speed Photography* (1982).

17. P.G. May, W. Sibbett, K.Smith, J.R. Taylor and J.P. Willson, *Opt. Commun.*, **42**, 285 (1982).

18. G. Mourou, B. Drouin and M. M. Denariez-Roberge, *Appl. Phys. Lett.*, **20**, 453 (1972).

19. G.E. Bush, K.S. Greve, G.L. Olsen, R.P. Jones and P.M. Rentzepis, *Chem.Phys.Lett.*, **33**, 417 (1975).

20. W. Sibbett, J.R. Taylor and D. Welford, *IEEE J. Quant.Elect.*, **QE-17**, 500 (1981).

21. H.E. Lessing and A.von Jena, *Chem.Phys.Lett.*, **42**, 213 (1976).

22. S.F. Mason, *J.Chem.Soc.*, 493 (1962).

23. G.H.C. New, *IEEE J. Quant. Elect.*, **QE-10**, 115 (1974).

24. W. Sibbett and J.R. Taylor, *IEEE J. Quant. Elect.*, **QE-19**, to be published (1983).

25. G. Oster and Y. Nishijima, *J. Am. Chem. Soc.*, **78**, 1581 (1956).

26. Th. Förster and G. Hoffmann, *Z. Phys. Chem.*, **NF75**, 63 (1971).

27. S. Schneider, E. Lill, P. Hefferle and F. Dörr, 'Laser Induced Processes in Molecules', *Chem. Phys.*, **6**, Springer-Verlag, 321 (1979).

28. W. Sibbett and J. R. Taylor, *Opt. Commun.*, **43**, 50 (1982).

29.   Th. Förster, *Discussions Faraday Soc.*, **27**, 7 (1959).

30.   M.C. Adams, .J. Bradley, W. Sibbett, and J.R. Taylor, *Chem.Phys.Lett.*, **66**, 428 (1979).

31.   D.J. Bradley, J. McInerney and J.R. Taylor, *Opt. Commun.*, to be published.

32.   B. Wilhelmi, *Chem. Phys.*, **66**, 351 (1982).

Viscosity - Dependent Internal Conversion in Polymethine Dyes measured by Picosecond Fluorescence Spectroscopy

A.C.Winkworth   and A.D.Osborne

Davy Faraday Research Laboratory, The Royal Institution, 21 Albemarle Street, London W1X 4BS

Introduction

Polymethine dyes are known to efficiently dissipate their electronic excitation energy by rapid internal conversion from their excited singlet state S_1[1]. The rate determining step in the deactivation process is the conformational relaxation in the excited state from the distribution existing immediately following excitation to the equilibrium conformation. This conformational change involves a twisting or torsional motion of the heterocyclic terminal groups about the linking aliphatic chain and gives rise to increased internal conversion rates as a consequence of the narrowing of the energy gap between the zeroth vibrational levels of the S_1 and S_0 electronic states.

The rate of conformational relaxation should show a strong dependence on processes which would tend to limit the twisting action of the end groups. Thus rigidification of the dye structure, for example, by cross-linking the heterocyclic rings, decreases the rate of internal conversion by maintaining the planarity of the molecule and thus leads to an increase in the fluorescence lifetime. Conversely, introduction of steric hindrance effects leads to an increase in the radiationless relaxation rate with a corresponding decrease in the fluorescence lifetime.

Since the conformational change in excited polymethine dye molecules involves the movement of a large moiety, frictional interaction with the solvent will be important. An increase in solvent viscosity would tend to hinder the twisting by increasing the effective rigidity of the molecular framework on the time-scale appropriate to electronic relaxation. The time interval between excitation and the achievement of those conformations that give rise to fast non-radiative decay is therefore longer whereas, in solvents of low viscosity, these conformations are reached more rapidly and fluorescence is quenched by the faster radiationless paths of relaxation.

The rate of internal conversion has been found to obey an empirical law of the form $\tau = C\eta^{\alpha}$ ^{2}, where τ is the relaxation lifetime, η is the viscosity and x, for a particular dye molecule, is strongly dependent on the type of solvent used.

We have measured the fluorescence lifetimes of a number of carbocyanine dyes, selected for their varying degrees of steric hindrance and size of substituent

groups, as a function of solvent viscosity, with a view to
gaining a fuller understanding of the mechanism of the
viscosity-dependent electronic relaxation in these and
related molecules.

Experimental

A detailed diagram showing the experimental arrangement
of the picosecond laser system used may be found elsewhere[3].
A mode-locked Nd:glass laser generates a train of approximately 100 pulses at a wavelength of 1060 nm; the pulses
have a typical duration of 6 ps and a pulse separation time
of 6.9 ns. The 1060 nm fundamental output is then converted
to 530 nm by a temperature-tuned CDA frequency-doubling
crystal. A Pöckels cell electro-optic shutter selects a
single pulse from the centre of the train which is then
subsequently delayed by a series of lenses and mirrors and
brought to a focus at the sample cell. Fluorescence emitted
by the sample is time-resolved by an Imacon 600 streak
camera with an S20 photocathode. After image intensification,
the fluorescence decay curves are digitised by a vidicon
optical multichannel analyser and transferred to the
computer for analysis.

Up to ten fluorescence traces were recorded for each
sample and summed within the computer. The measured decays
were all found to fit a single exponential convoluted with
the instrument response function (Figure 1). In general,
concentrations of dye were selected to give an optical

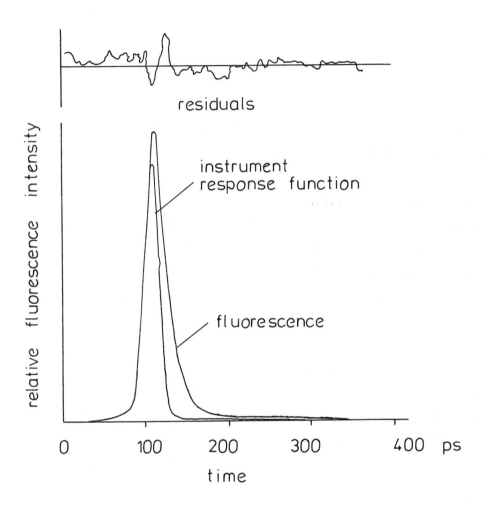

Figure 1

Example of fluorescence decay convoluted with the instrument response function.

density < 0.5 in a 1 mm cuvette. To preclude self-aggregation, self-absorption of fluorescence or stimulated emission, dye concentrations were kept below 10^{-4}M. Figure 2 shows the structures of the dyes whose fluorescence life times are reported here.

Results and Observations

Table 1 shows the results of measurements of τ in a series of aliphatic monols, diols and, in some cases, glycerol. These data are plotted in Figures 3 and 4 on log-log diagrams whose slopes give the value of the viscosity power dependence α.

From the data we note the following:

1) τ in the group I to III are similar, indicating that the size of the N-alkyl group and the nature of the counterion do not significantly affect the rate of internal conversion, excluding the unlikely event that the size of the N-alkyl group and the nature of the counterion have exactly equal and opposite effects.

2) IV and V both have significantly smaller τ than I, II and III, a consequence of the relatively weaker conjugation in their polymethine chains.

DQOCI (V) is an asymmetric carbocyanine[2],

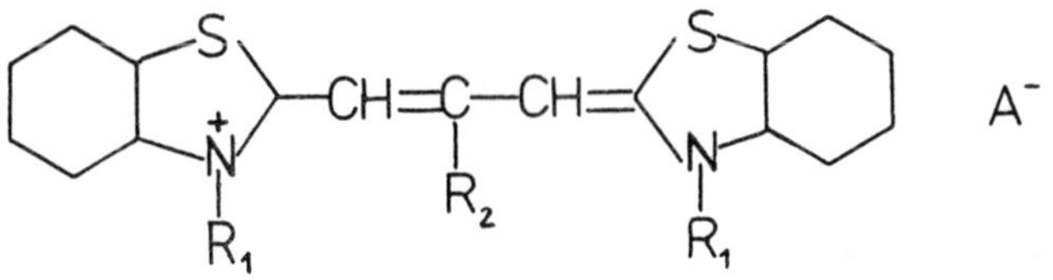

	R₁	R₂	A⁻
I	CH₃	H	tosyl
II	C₂H₅	H	I⁻
III	C₃H₅	H	Br⁻

IV

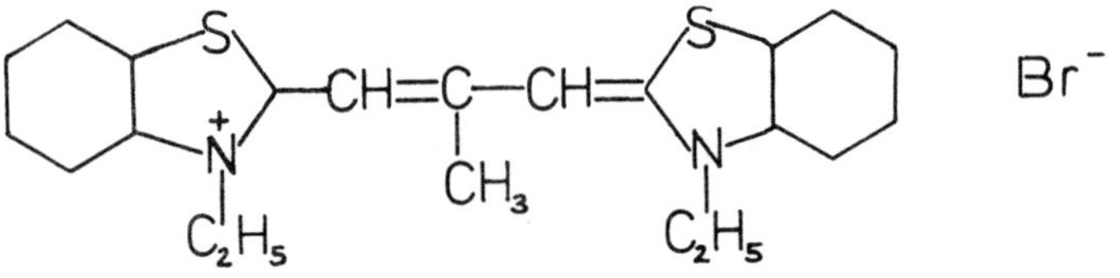

3,3'-diethyl-9-methyl thiacarbocyanine bromide

V

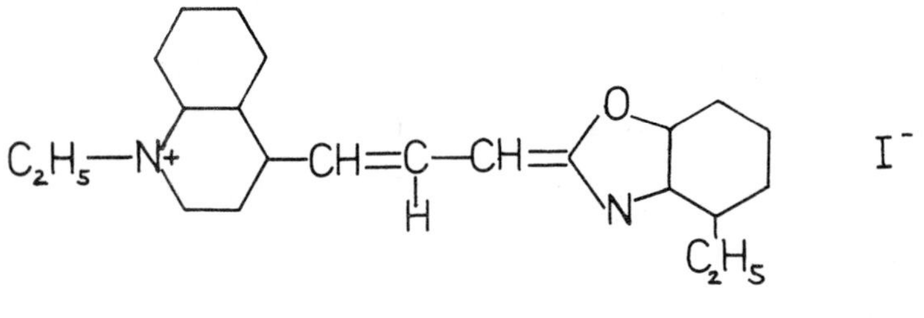

1,3-diethyl-4,2-quinolyloxacarbocyanine iodide

Figure 2   Structures of polymethine dyes used.

Table 1 Fluorescence lifetimes (ps): viscosity (cP)

solvent	viscosity	I	II	III	IV	V
methanol	0.55	92	125	137	12	11
ethanol	1.2	149	173	227	19	20
propan-1-ol	2.0	182	261	270	22	33
propan-2-ol	2.4	156	262	261	25	35
butanol	2.6	254	302	354	32	49
pentanol	4.0	381	371	415	43	73
hexanol	5.4	353	482	545	63	111
heptanol	7.0	406	524	644	79	145
octanol	8.8	448	627	742	125	196
nonanol	10.3	524	641	692	157	247
decanol	12.3	553	756	814	175	316
undecanol	14.2	575	798	808	214	389
cyclohexanol	33	562	884	889	171	367
ethan-1,2-diol	20	390	603	526	104	137
propan-1,2-diol	40	480	811	840	155	224
pentan-1,5-diol	98				257	470
pentan-1,4-diol	163				336	654
glycerol	900				886	1104

Fluorescence lifetime measurements for dyes I to V.

234

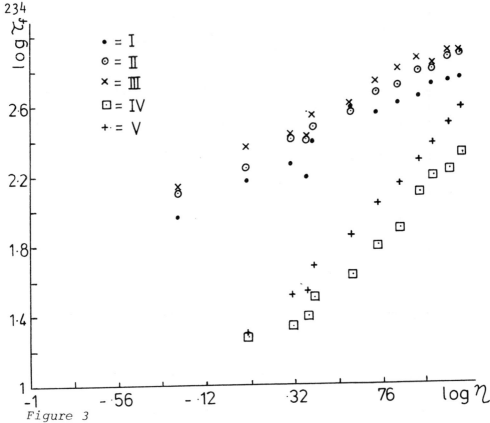

Figure 3

Log-log plot of fluorescence lifetime (τ_f) against viscosity (η) for the dyes I to V in a homolgous series of monohydric alcohols.

dissimilar contributions being made by each ring system to the canonical forms of the dye[4]. Consequently, double bond character is localised at various positions along the polymethine chain and this reduces its resonance stabilisation. Thus, in fluid solvents, the dye readily rotates out of coplanarity, giving rise to short fluorescence lifetimes.

In DMTCB (IV), on the other hand, the relatively weak conjugation in the polymethine chain is due, not to asymmetry,

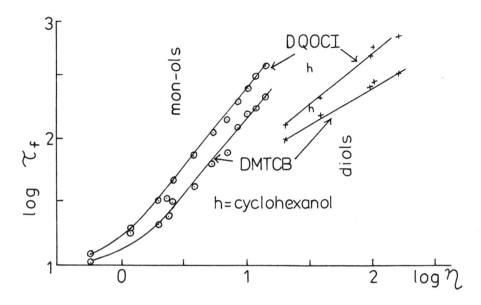

Figure 4

   Log-log plot of fluorescence lifetime (τ_f) against viscosity (η) for dyes IV and V in a series of aliphatic monols and diols.

but to steric hindrance between the methyl substituent in the chain and the N-ethyl groups[5]. In the absence of the -CH$_3$ group, any crowding existing in the molecule can be accommodated without substantial departure from coplanarity by minor adjustments of the bond angles. If the hydrogen of the = CH - group is replaced by an alkyl radical, however, considerable overlapping of the spheres of interference of the constituent atoms of the heterocyclic groups and the polymethine chain occurs, resulting in increased crowding in the molecule, even when the group introduced at the centre is methyl.

3)   The viscosity power dependence, α, varies with the
      structure of the dye molecule, i.e., $\alpha = 1.25$ for
      IV and V, whereas $\alpha \sim 0.6$ for I, II and III in
      monohydric alcohols.

4)   The value of α is lower in the diols than in the
      monols, for example, for IV and V, the η dependence
      of the fluorescence lifetime in a series of aliphatic
      diols is of the form $\tau = C\eta^{\alpha}$, with α in the range
      0.6 to 0.78. However, in the monohydric alcohols,
      $\alpha = 1.25$, as already mentioned above.

5)   Internal conversion is anomalously fast in the
      diols and glycerol, as was found for the N-aryl
      substituted rhodamine dyes[6,7], indicating that
      it is micro-environment rather than bulk
      viscosity which is of greater importance.

The microviscosity of a solvent encompasses a
number of factors, namely the motion of solvent molecules
out of the path of the rotating group in question, the
strength and rate of breaking of dye: solvent and solvent:
solvent hydrogen bonds and the size of the gaps in the
solvent relative to the size of the rotating group which
mediates radiationless conversion to the ground state.
Since microviscosity is so dependent upon the properties
of the fluorescent species, there can be no unique
microviscosity for a particular solvent, so that
comparisons based upon bulk viscosity may only be made on
a semi-quantitative level.

A qualitative explanation for the anomalous behaviour in diols is that there is very strong solvent: solvent, but only comparatively weak, dye: solvent H-bonding, so that internal rotations can occur relatively freely within a rigid solvent cage.

The anomalously low values of τ in the diols and glycerol may be able to explain why, for the same dye, it is observed that α is smaller in mixed solvents than in the separate pure components.

Various studies of the viscosity-dependence of the rate of internal conversion in mixed solvents have been reported. In ethanol/glycerol mixtures it is found that the viscosity power dependence varies between 0.35 and 0.7[8]. A recent study, using both mixed solvents and a homologous series of unbranched alcohols, established that α approaches 0.5 in the former but is close to unity in the latter[9].

If one mixes solvents lying on different τ vs η curves, then it might be expected that the resultant mixture would show an η dependence somewhere in between those of the separate components.

To test this hypothesis, the fluorescence lifetime of I in various mixtures of heptanol and 1,2 - propane diol was measured. τ was found to be independent of the composition of the mixture.

Discussion and Conclusion

Various theories have been developed that attempt to explain the experimental data that have been reported on viscosity-dependent internal conversion rates of several types of polyatomic molecule, notably polymethine and triphenylmethane dyes.

Oster and Nishijima[10] examined the effect of solvent viscosity and temperature on the fluorescence quantum yield of auramine O, a substituted diphenylmethane dye, and proposed that it should vary as η/T. This suggested that fluorescence quenching was linked to a diffusion-controlled process. Oster and Nishijima concluded that auramine O fluorescence was quenched by internal conversion resulting from phenyl ring rotation. In viscous media, the ring rotation was hindered and internal conversion less efficient, resulting in greater fluorescence quantum yields.

However, it is not proper to describe the motion in terms of a random, thermally driven process if, as Oster and Nishijima suggest, the dissipation of electronic energy is by phenyl ring rotational motion. Clearly, some directed mechanism must exist within the molecule to account for these motions.

According to Förster and Hoffmann[11], who evaluated the effects of temperature and viscosity on the absorption and fluorescence spectra of several substituted triphenylmethane dyes, the fluorescence quantum yield should vary as $\eta^{2/3}$. In their model, they considered a damped oscillation of the phenyl groups in a potential well created by intramolecular forces and assumed that the radiationless relaxation rate varied as $(\Theta - \Theta_0)^2$, where Θ_0 is the equilibrium dihedral angle of the ground state. This assumption led to a rate law for the decay of S_1 of the form $\exp(-at^3)$, which has never been observed by time-resolved fluorescence spectroscopy[12]. So, although the Förster-Hoffmann model appears to be correct on a qualitative level, it fails to predict the observed kinetics of relaxation.

Recently, McCaskill and Gilbert[13] showed that experimental data for the picosecond conformational relaxation of a large molecule could be modelled very successfully using the unabbreviated Fokker-Planck equation[14]. They proposed a hydro-dynamic model that was able to successfully interpret the non-linear viscosity/relaxation time dependence of 1,1 - binaphthyl. Their model was based upon passage of the initial Franck Condon state over a small barrier to a second excited state from which radiationless conversion to S_0 was very efficient, and incorporated a coupling between viscous and inertial effects in addition to thermally-induced motion into the description of the rate coefficient for passage over the barrier.

An attempt was made by Osborne[15] to fit the results of fluorescence lifetime measurements of FAV2R in a series of alcohols into a scheme similar to that of McCaskill and Gilbert, in which the state from which fluorescence occured could relax by means of an internal torsional movement, to a conformation from which radiationless decay to the ground state was very rapid. The torsional motion was hindered by viscous drag in the solvent.

Osborne concluded that the model gave rise to a $T = fn. (\eta)$ which was more complex than the simple empirical law: $T = C\eta^{2/3}$, but approximated to a two-thirds power dependence if it was assumed that the effective reduced moment of inertia increased with the molecular weight of the solvent, an effect which was consistent with there being some solvent attachment. In the absence of such an effect, the theoretical curves showed a power dependence higher than 2/3. This model therefore provides an explanation for the anomalously low rates of internal conversion in diols.

Wilhelmi[16] also considered the McCaskill and Gilbert model and concluded that low values of $\propto$ were due to a viscosity-independent channel for internal conversion.

Although the McCaskill and Gilbert model can successfully interpret many of the experimental results, it does not explain why, for solvents having different viscosities, the relaxation rates can be identical and it fails to predict values of α greater than unity. From experimental data on polymethine dyes, there is evidence to suggest that in these molecules there is no intramolecular potential barrier so that the McCaskill and Gilbert model is not readily applicable to these dyes.

To date then, no one model can successfully reproduce all of the experimental characteristics of viscosity-dependent internal conversion, although consideration of each in turn does give us a greater insight into the nature and complexity of the dependence of this deactivation process on solvent change.

Acknowledgement
We acknowledge financial support from the SERC.

242

References

1. A.V. Buettner, *J. Chem. Phys.*, **46**, (1967), 1398.

2. C.J. Tredwell and C.M. Keary, *Chem. Phys.*, **43**, (1979), 307.

3. M.D. Archer, M.I.C. Ferreira, G. Porter and C.J. Tredwell, *Nouveau Journal de Chimie*, 1, (1977), 9.

4. A. Weissberger and E.C. Taylor, *(Eds.), Special Topics in Heterocyclic Chemistry*, (Wiley-Interscience, New York), **30**, (1977), 441.

5. L.G.S. Brooker, F.L. White, R.H. Sprague, S.G. Dent,Jr., and G. van Zandt, *Chem. Rev.*, (1947), 325.

6. C.J. Tredwell and A.D. Osborne, *J.C.S. Faraday II*, **76**, (1980), 1627.

7. A.D. Osborne and A.C. Winkworth, *Chem. Phys. Lett.*, **85**, (1982), 513.

8 W. Sibbett, J.R. Taylor and D. Welford, *I.E.E.E.J. Quantum Electronics*, Q.E. **17**:4, (1981), 500.

9. V. Sundström and T. Gillbro, *Chem.Phys.*, **61**, (1981),257.

10. G. Oster and Y. Nishijima, *J.Am. Chem.Soc.*, **78**, (1956), 1581.

11. Th. Förster and G. Hoffmann, *Z. Phys. Chem. N.F.*, **75**, (1971), 63.

12. D.A. Cremers and M.W. Windsor, *Chem. Phys. Lett.*, **71**, (1980), 27.

13. J.C.S. McCaskill and R.G. Gilbert, *Chem. Phys.*, **44**, (1979), 389.

14. H.A. Kramers, *Physica*, (1940), 284.

15. A.D. Osborne, *J.C.S. Faraday II,* **76**, (1980), 1638.

16. B. Wilhelmi, *Chem.Phys.,* **66**, (1982), 351.

Subnanosecond Decaytime Measurement using a Coaxial Flashlamp

D.J.S. Birch and R.E. Imhof

Department of Applied Physics, Strathclyde University, Glasgow, Scotland

Abstract

We have developed a low cost thyratron gated flashlamp capable of generating reproducible optical pulses down to 0.5 ns FWHM. This performance is achieved by combining an all metal transmission line geometry with a stability monitor which correlates every thyratron gating pulse and lamp flash. The instrumental profile under single photon conditions using an XP2020Q photomultiplier has a FWHM of 0.8 ns. A synchronously pumped dye laser of pulse duration 10 ps gave similar instrumental profiles of 0.6 ns FWHM. The application of such a flashlamp to study the effect of solvent on the photoisomerisation of butadiene derivatives shows that decay times down to 200 ps can be routinely determined with high precision. Data on rose bengal (decay time 0.76 ± 0.01 ns) excited at 555 nm illustrates that such measurements are not restricted to the UV.

Introduction

Nanosecond flashlamps are the most widely used sources for fluorescence decay time measurements[1]. This is not surprising since they are of low cost, easily tunable and of appropriate intensity and pulse width for most applications. However, the study of sub-nanosecond phenomena places stringent demands on the optical source and conventional gated flashlamps can be unsatisfactory for the following reasons:

1) *Pulse width* - typically a few nanoseconds requiring a large emphasis on deconvolution procedures.

2) *RF interference* - high voltage switching on a sub-nanosecond time scale generates rf emission which causes oscillations on measured decay curves.

3) *Reproducibility* - a spark breakdown can be erratic and does not always follow a trigger pulse. This can invalidate deconvolution analysis.

4) *Intensity* - typically 10^9 photons per pulse. This precludes the use and study of non linear optical phenomena. Low quantum yields can still be studied by increasing the data accumulation time provided the flashlamp is stable.

With these points in mind we have constructed a flashlamp system which permits high resolution sub-nanosecond decay time measurements down to 200 ps[2].

Flashlamp Design

Figure 1 shows a cross section through the flashlamp. It
incorporates a transmission line geometry which preserves a
constant wave impedance along the conducting path. This
minimises reflections, thus obtaining a maximum optical
output of minimum duration. The flashlamp is of an all
metal construction as shown in the photograph in figure 2.
Flashlamps are usually constructed of glass or other
insulating material which is transparent to rf. These
require a Faraday cage and extensive filtering to try and
reduce rf leakage. The all metal design eliminates rf
leakage problems at source.

Stability Monitor

The single photon technique involves correlating an
excitation pulse with single fluorescence photons from a
decay using a time to amplitude converter. To ensure stable
flashlamp operations we have introduced a second correlation
measurement into the traditional photon counting arrangement.
This stability monitor is shown in figure 3. Every gating
pulse sent to the thyratron is correlated with every optical
pulse using logic circuitry. Should a spark breakdown not
occur following a gating pulse, a warning LED is momentarily
turned on to indicate a 'misfire' event. Should an optical
pulse occur which is not related to a gating pulse, another
LED is momentarily turned on to indicate a 'free-run' event.

The monitor is valuable in optimising the flashlamp

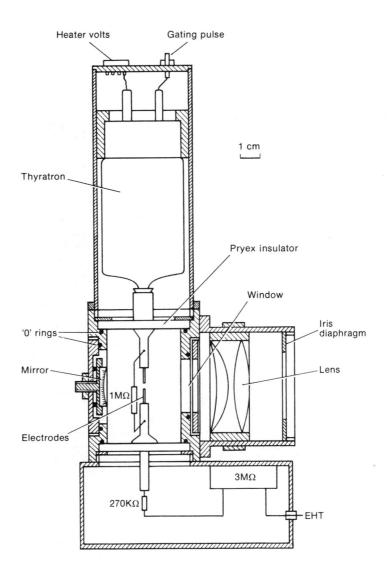

Figure 1   Cross section through the Flashlamp

248

Figure 2

   Flashlamp and synchronisation photomultiplier

parameters (voltage, spark gap, repetition rate, etc.) for
a particular application. It also provides early
recognition of electrode erosion and deteriorating pulse
to pulse reproducibility after prolonged operation. Such
a technique is far more sensitive and convenient than
using rate meters or scalers to compare signal rates,
since it can register single 'misfire' and 'free-run'
events directly.

Pulse Profiles

Figure 4 compares the instrumental pulse profile for
hydrogen and nitrogen as filler gases. The measurements
were made under single photon conditions using an XP2020Q
photomultiplier. The FWHM is 0.8 and 1 ns for hydrogen
and nitrogen respectively. The flashlamp repetition rate
was 30 kHz, though at 100 kHz the coaxial geometry ensures
an increase in FWHM of only 0.2 ns under suitable conditions.

Figure 5 compares the hydrogen pulse with that obtained
using a mode locked argon ion laser to synchronously pump
a dye laser (Coherent Radiation). The laser pulse duration
is $\sim$ 10 ps but the single photon detection technique limits
the instrumental width to $\sim$ 0.6 ns. Deconvolution
techniques are thus still necessary for any sub-nanosecond
decay. This illustrates that with the single photon
technique, ps lasers offer only slight improvement in time
resolution at over an order of magnitude increase in cost.

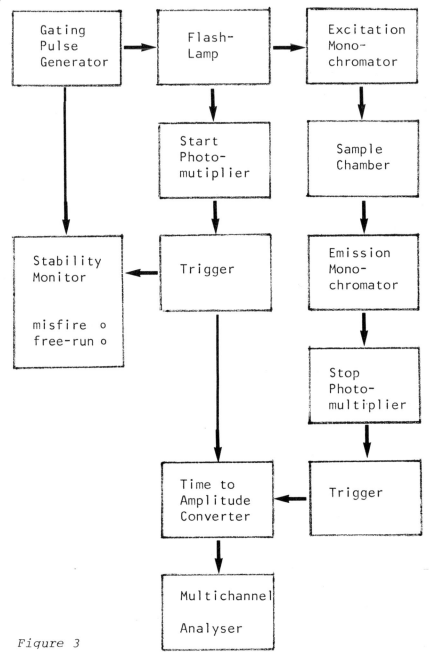

Figure 3

Schematic diagram of the single-photon and monitor
coincidence arrangements

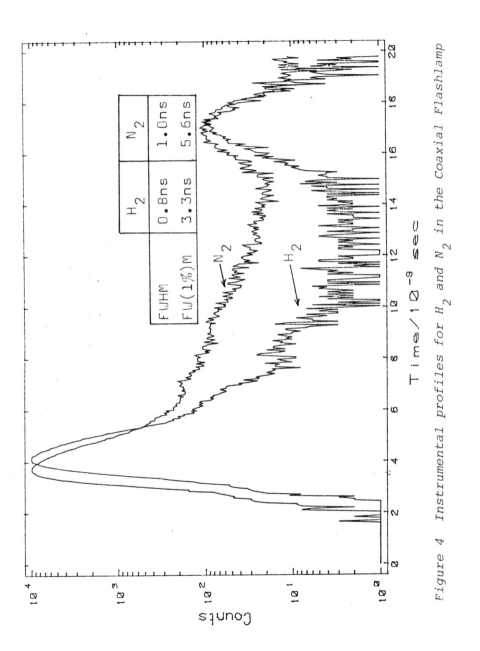

Figure 4   Instrumental profiles for H_2 and N_2 in the Coaxial Flashlamp

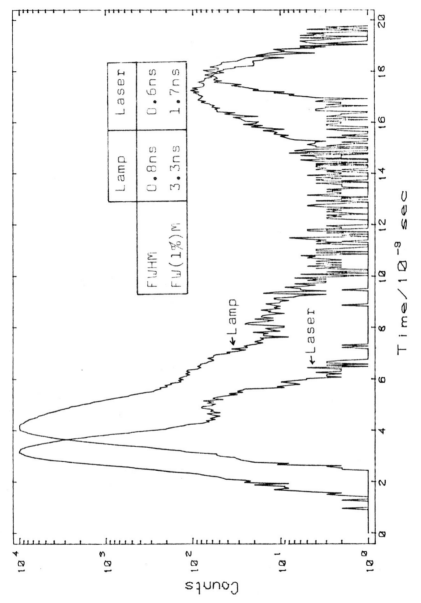

Figure 5   *Instrumental profiles for H_2 Coaxial Lamp and ps Dye Laser*

Sub-nanosecond Decays

Polyenes possess a number of interesting fluorescence properties not observed in more rigid aromatic molecules[3]. The most widely studied of these is photoisomerisation. The rate of photoisomerisation depends on temperature, solvent viscosity and specific excited state interactions with the solvent cage[4].

Trans-trans diphenylbutadiene (DPB) is a polyene widely used as a scintillator with possible applications as a saturable absorber for mode locking UV lasers. The tetraphenyl derivative (TPB) has a very broad emission spectrum and is useful as a wavelength shifter. Both molecules undergo photoisomerisation. The table below shows the fluorescence decay times for DPB in methylcylclohexane isohexane (MCH/IH) and propylene glycol (PG)as a function of temperature.

$$\tau_F \text{(ns)}$$

Temperature (^{O}C)	MCH/IH	PG
+75	0.21	0.07
+50	0.31	0.08
+25	0.49	0.20
0	0.73	0.46
-25	0.93	0.88
-50	1.02	1.09

These data were obtained using the coaxial flashlamp in a double monochrometer fluorometer (exc 320nm, em 380nm) with

reconvolution analysis. The standard deviation for all
these decay times is <10ps. The radiative rate parameter
K_F $(=\phi/\tau_F)$ is shown in figure 6. K_F in both solvents is
seen to be constant to within ± 10% at all temperatures
up to + 50°C. This is what would be expected for more
rigid molecules with only a slight K_F variation in
accordance with the refractive index change. The decrease
in τ_F with increasing temperature is associated with an
increase in the rate of photoisomerisation. K_F at + 75°C
in both solvents is away from the general trend and we
associate this with the limit of time resolution for
routine measurement, i.e. $\sim$ 200 ps. On this sort of time
scale other effects in addition to flashlamp stability
start to be important, e.g. wavelength dependence of
photon transit time dispersion in the photomultiplier[5]
and diffraction grating[6] geometrical effects etc.

Sub-nanosecond decays can be clearly resolved from the
instrumental pulse as well as from each other as shown in
figure 7. Figure 8 shows the least squares fit to the
200 ps decay of DPB in PG at 25°C using a single
exponential model. The random distribution of residuals
and normalised chi-squared of 1.14 indicate both the
appropriateness of the single exponential decay model and
the stability of the flashlamp.

TPB is found to have a decay time which is more
strongly dependent on solvent: 1.5 ns in MCH/IH, 0.27 ns

255

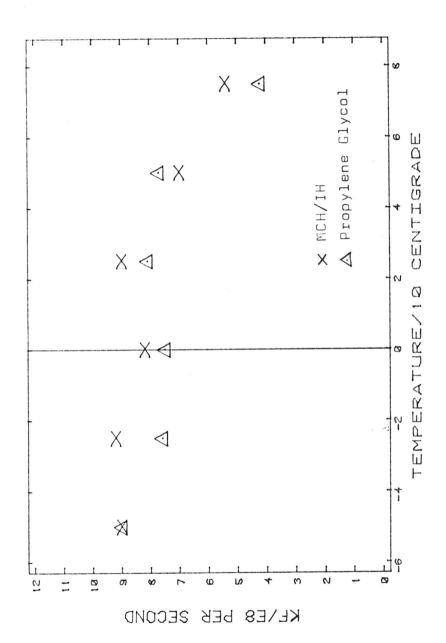

Figure 6   Variation of k_F for DPB with Temperature

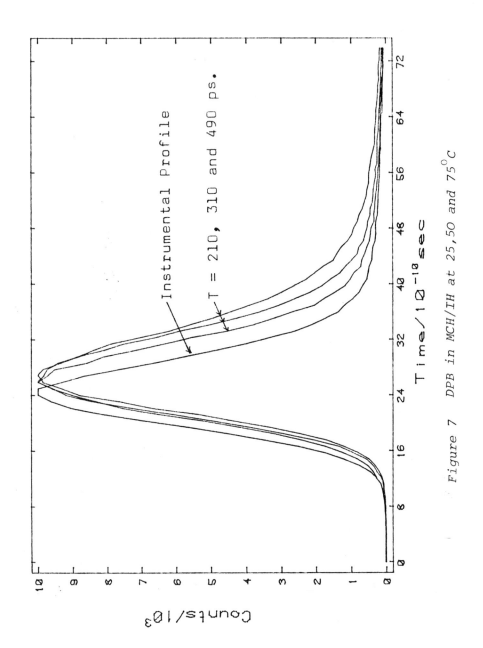

Figure 7   DPB in MCH/IH at 25,50 and 75°C

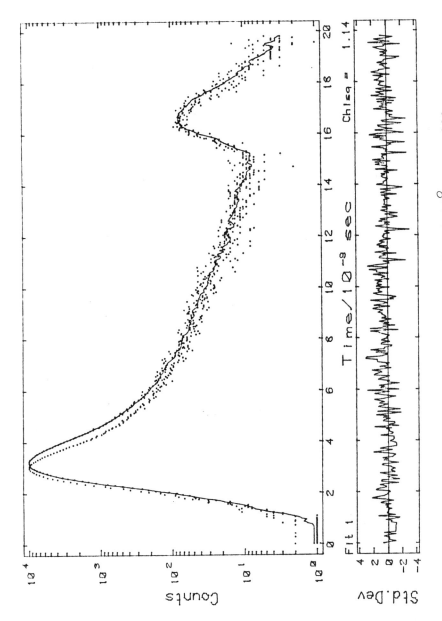

Figure 8   DPB in Propylene Glycol 25°C   T = 200 ps

in PG, 0.24 ns in benzene and 0.34 ns in toluene. However, we have found some evidence of non-exponential decay in this molecule and further work is in progress to determine if emission is occuring from photoisomers.

That this time resolution is not limited to UV excitation with coaxial flashlamps is illustrated in figure 9 which shows the room temperature decay of rose bengal in ethanol, $\tau = 0.76 \pm 0.01$ ns. The excitation wavelength is 555 nm and the emission at 583 nm. Second order excitation light at 277.5 nm was excluded by means of a glass filter. The data was accumulated for 45 minutes and gave a normalised chi-squared of 1.08.

Acknowledgement

We would like to thank Dr H. Leismann for providing the zone refined rose bengal and the SERC for their support.

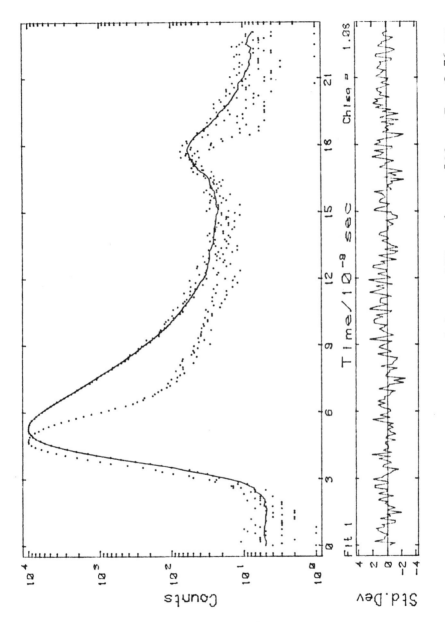

Figure 9   Rose Bengal in Ethanol $\lambda ex = 555nm$, $\lambda em = 583nm$ $T = 0.76$ ns

References

1) M.A. West and G.S. Beddard, *International Laboratory*, **61**, May/June (1975).

2) D.J.S. Birch and R.E. Imhof, *Rev.Sci.Instrum.* **52**, 1206 (1981).

3) J.B.Birks and D.J.S. Birch, *Chem.Phys.Letters*, **31**, 608 (1975).

4) J. Saltiel, J.D'Agostino, E.D. Megarity, L. Metts, K.R. Neuberger, M. Wrighton and O.C. Zofarion, *Org. Photochem.* **3**,1 (1971).

5) Ph. Wahl, J.C. Auchet and B. Donzel, *Rev.Sci.Instrum.* **45**, 28 (1974).

6) R.E. Imhof and D.J.S. Birch, *Optics Comm.* **42**, 83 (1982).

BIBLIOGRAPHY 1983

H. Masuhara, H. Miyasaka, A. Karen, T. Uemiya, N. Mataga, M. Koishi, A. Takeshima and Y. Tsuchiya, Opt. Commun., (1983), 44, 426. 'Temporal characteristics of picosecond continuum as revealed by a two-dimensional analysis of streak images.'

N. A. Borisevich, S. A. Tikhomirov and G. B. Tolstorozhev, Dokl. Akad. Nauk SSSR, (1983), 268, 344; Chem. Abstr. 98-134591. 'Picosecond kinetics of induced singlet-singlet absorption spectra of complex molecule vapors.'

D. A. Cremers and T. L. Cremers, Chem. Phys. Lett., (1983), 94, 102. 'Picosecond dynamics of conformation changes in malachite green leucocyanide.'

K. Kamogawa, J. M. Morris, Y. Takagi, N. Nakashima, K. Yoshihara and I. Ikegami, Photochem. Photobiol., (1983), 37, 207. 'Picosecond fluorescence studies of P700-enriched particles of spinach chloroplasts.'

N. Ikeda, N. Mataga, U. Steiner and M. H. Abdel-Kader, Chem. Phys. Lett., (1983), 95, 66. 'Picosecond laser photolysis studies upon photochemical isomerization and protolytic reaction of a stilbazolium betaine.'

A. N. Rubinov, B. A. Bushuk, A. A. Murav'ov and A. P. Stupak, Appl. Phys. Part B, (1983), B30, 99. 'Picosecond spectroscopy of intramolecular interactions in dye solutions.'

H. L. Fang, T. L. Gustafson and R. L. Swofford, J. Chem. Phys., (1983), 78, 1663. 'Two-photon absorption photothermal spectroscopy using a synchronously pumped picosecond dye laser. Thermal lensing spectra of naphthalene and diphenylbutadiene.'

V. Sundstroem and T. Gillbro, Chem. Phys. Lett., (1983), 94, 580. 'Transient absorption spectra of pinacyanol and cyanine photoisomers obtained with a sync-pumped picosecond dye laser and independently tunable probe light.'

L. V. Haley and J. A. Koningstein, Chem. Phys., (1983), 73, 263. 'Raman spectroscopy from a picosecond-lived excited state of methyl orange.'

T. Okamura, M. Sumitani and K. Yoshihara, Chem. Phys. Lett., (1983), 94, 339. 'Picosecond dynamic Stokes shift of alpha-naphthylamine.'

Y. Suzuki and M. Hirai, Semicond. Insul., (1983), 5, 445. 'Picosecond spectroscopic studies on defect formation in alkali halides.'

P. M. Felker and A. H. Zewail, Chem. Phys. Lett., (1983), 94, 454. 'Stepwise solvation of molecules as studies by picosecond-jet spectroscopy : dynamics and spectra.'

P. A. Cornelius, R. M. Hochstrasser and A. W. Steele, J. Mol. Biol., (1983), 163, 119. 'Ultrafast relaxation in picosecond photolysis of nitrosylhemoglobin.'

BIBLIOGRAPHY 1983

R. Gadonas, R. Danielius, A. Piskarskas and S. Rentsch, Kvant. Elektron, (1983), 10, 341; Chem. Abstr. 98-188687. 'Ultrafast photophysical phenomenon in cyanine dyes during picosecond excitation with tunable wavelength'

R.J.D. Miller, M. Pierre and M.D. Fayer, J. Chem. Phys., (1983), 78, 5138. 'Electronic excited state transport and trapping in diordered systems : picosecond fluorescence mixing, transient grating, and probe pulse experiments'

A.M. Freiberg and K.E. Timpmann, Pis'ma Zh. Eksp. Teor. Fiz., (1983), 37, 209; Chem. Abstr. 98-188431. 'Direct observation of picosecond relaxation of high electronic states of some dye molecules in solution'

G. Marowsky, P. Anliker and Q. Munir, Opt. Commun., (1983), 45, 183. 'Picosecond CARS study of the nu-2 band of liquid benzene'

W. Haehnel, A.R. Holzwarth and J. Wendler, Photochem. Photobiol., (1983), 37, 435. 'Picosecond fluorescence kinetics and energy transfer in the antenna chlorophylls of green algae'

K. Yagi, F. Tanaka, N. Nakashima and K. Yoshihara, J. Biol. Chem., (1983), 258, 3799. 'Picosecond laser fluorometry of FAD of D-amino acid oxidase-benzoate complex'

P.Y. Lu, Z.X. Yu, R.R. Alfano and J.I. Gersten, Phys. Rev. A., (1983), 27, 2100. 'Picosecond studies of energy transfer of donor and acceptor dye molecules in solution. II. A concentration dependence'

H. Staerk, R. Mitzkus, H. Meyer and A. Weller, Appl. Phys. Part B, (1983), B30, 153. 'Picosecond streak camera performance in studies of exciplex formation dynamics.'

W. Zinth and W. Kaiser, Kvant. Elektron, (1983), 10, 44; Chem. Abstr. 98-152025. 'New method for studying polyatomic molecules in liquids using picosecond light pulses.'

H. Masuhara, N. Tamai, N. Mataga, F. C. De Schryver, J. Vandendriessche and N. Boens, Chem. Phys. Lett., (1983), 95, 471. 'Excimer formation in poly(N-vinylcarbazole) and its model compounds as revealed by picosecond time-resolved absorption spectroscopy.'

D. F. Kelly and P. M. Rentzepis, J. Am. Chem. Soc., (1983), 105, 1820. 'Picosecond emmision spectroscopy of two predissociative isomeric methylenepyrazolines and product trimethylenemethane.'

Y. I. Nissim, J. Sapriel and J. L. Oudar, Appl. Phys. Lett., (1983), 42, 504. 'Microprobe Raman analysis of picosecond laser annealed implanted silicon.'

Y. Takagi, M. Sumitani, N. Nakashima, D. V. O'Connor and K. Yoshihara, Appl. Phys. Lett., (1983), 42, 489. 'Generation of high-power picosecond continuosly tunable radiation between 215 and 245 nm by mixing of Raman and optical parametric light.'

BIBLIOGRAPHY 1982

D. Reiser and A. Laubereau, <u>Ber. Bunsenges. Phys. Chem</u>., (1982), <u>86</u>, 1106. 'Picosecond polarization spectroscopy of dye molecules.'

H. Staerk, R. Mitzkus, W. Kuehnle and A. Weller, <u>Springer Ser. Chem. Phys</u>., (1982), <u>23</u>, 205. 'Picosecond studies of intramolecular charge transfer processes in excited A-D molecules.'

J. C. Mialocq, <u>Chem. Phys</u>., (1982), <u>73</u>, 107. 'Picosecond study of pinacyanol photophysics.'

Y. Wang and K. B. Eisenthal, <u>J. Chem. Phys</u>., (1982), <u>77</u>, 6076. 'Picosecond dynamics of twisted internal charge transfer phenomena. The role of the solvent.'

A. H. Zewail, <u>Springer Ser. Chem. Phys</u>., (1982), <u>23</u>, 184. 'Picosecond laser spectroscopy of molecules in supersonic jets : vibrational energy redistribution and quantum beats.'

D. D. Dlott, C. L. Schosser and E. L. Chronister, <u>Chem. Phys. Lett</u>., (1982), <u>90</u>, 386. 'Temperature dependent vibrational dephasing in molecular crystals : a picosecond CARS study of naphthalene.'

J. D. Simon and K. S. Peters, <u>J. Am. Chem. Soc</u>., (1982), <u>104</u>, 6542. 'Picosecond dynamics of ion pairs : the effect of hydrogen bonding on ion-pair intermediates.'

P. E. Schoen, M. J. Marrone and L. S. Goldberg, <u>Springer Ser. Chem. Phys</u>., (1982), <u>23</u>, 269. 'Picosecond laser induced fluorescence probing of monomeric nitrogen dioxide photofragments.'

M. D. Fayer, <u>Springer Ser. Chem. Phys</u>., (1982), <u>23</u>, 82. 'Picosecond holographic grating experiments in molecular condensed phases.'

J. Kuhl and D. Von der Linde, <u>Springer Ser. Chem. Phys</u>., (1982), <u>23</u>, 201. 'A picosecond CARS-spectrometer using two synchronously mode-locked CW dye lasers.'

A. L. Huston and G. W. Scott, <u>Proc. SPIE-Int. Soc. Opt. Eng</u>., (1982), <u>322</u>, 215. 'Picosecond kinetics of excited state decay processes in internally hydrogen-bonded polymer photostabilisers.'

O.D. Dmitrievskii, <u>Vozbuzhdennye Mol</u>., (1982), pp. 249-55; <u>Chem. Abstr</u>. 98-188138. 'Fast spectrometry and some of its applications'

P. Reisberg, J. A. Nairn and K. Sauer, <u>Photochem. Photobiol</u>., (1982), <u>36</u>, 657. 'Picosecond fluorescence kinetics in spinach chloroplasts at low temperature.'

B. N. Korvatovskii, V. Z. Pashchenko, A. B. Rubin, L. B. Rubin and V. B. Tusov, <u>Biol. Nauki</u>., (1982), <u>11</u>, 105; <u>Chem. Abstr</u>. 98-085521. Automatic pulsed fluorometer with short resolution time and high sensitivity.'

BIBLIOGRAPHY 1982

J. A. Nairn, W. Haehnel, P. Reisberg and K. Sauer, Biochim. Biophys. Acta., (1982), 682, 420. 'Picosecond fluorescence kinetics in spinach chloroplasts at room temperature. Effects of magnesium ion.'

R. J. Gulotty, G. R. Fleming and R. S. Alberte, Biochim. Biophys. Acta. (1982), 682, 322. 'Low-intensity picosecond fluorescence kinetics and excitation dynamics in barley chloroplasts.'

M. E. Lippitsch, M. Riegler, A. Leitner and F. R. Aussenegg, Springer Series Chem. Phys., (1982), 23, 323. 'Picosecond absorption spectroscopy of biliverdin.'

J. Terner, T. G. Spiro, D. F. Voss, C. Paddock and R. B. Miles, Spinger Series Chem. Phys., (1982), 23, 327. 'Picosecond time-resolved resonance Raman spectroscopy of the photolysis product of oxyhemoglobin.'

M. E. Lippitsch, M. Riegler, F. R. Aussenegg, L. Margulies and Y. Mazur, Springer Ser. Chem. Phys., (1982), 23, 319. 'Picosecond linear dichroism spectroscopy of retinal.'

P. A. Cornelius and R. M. Hochstrasser, Springer Ser. Chem. Phys., (1982), 23, 288. 'Picosecond processes involving carbon monoxide, oxygen, and nitric oxide derivatives of heme proteins.'

W. Knox, T. M. Nordlund and G. Mourou, Springer Ser. Chem. Phys., (1982), 23, 98. 'Jitter-free streak camera system.'

P. Bado, P. H. Berens and K. R. Wilson, Proc. SPIE-Int. Soc. Opt. Eng., (1982), 322, 230. 'Picosecond dynamics of solution reactions.'

A. Seilmeier, B. Kopainsky, W. Kranitzky, W. Kaiser and K. H. Drexhage, Springer Ser. Chem. Phys., (1982), 23, 23. 'New infrared dyes for synchronously pumped picosecond lasers.'

D.V. O'Connor, M. Sumitani, J. M. Morris and K. Yoshihara, Chem. Phys. Lett., (1982), 93, 350. 'Non-exponential picosecond fluorescence decay in isolated pentafluorobenzene and hexafluorobenzene.'

D. Hulin, A. Antonetti, L. L. Chase, G. Hamoniaux, A. Migus and A. Mysyrowicz, Springer Ser. Chem. Phys., (1982), 23, 345. 'Picosecond time-resolved study of highly excited copper(1)chloride.'

M. Yamashita, T. Sato, K. Aizawa and H. Kato, Springer Ser. Chem. Phys., (1982), 23, 298. 'Picosecond fluorescence spectroscopy of hematoporphyrin derivatives and related porphyrins.'

K. G. Spears, T. H. Gray and D. Huang, Springer Ser. Chem. Phys., (1982), 23, 278. 'Picosecond dynamics of unimolecular ion pair formation.'

BIBLIOGRAPHY 1982

B. A. Bushuk, A. N. Rubinov, A. A. Murav'ev and A. P. Stupak, Springer Ser. Chem. Phys., (1982), 23, 246. 'Kinetics of stimulated and spontaneous emmision of dye solutions under picosecond excitation.'

A. C. Winkworth, A. D. Osborne and G. Porter, Springer Ser. Chem. Phys., (1982), 23, 228. 'Viscosity-dependent internal rotation in polymethine dyes measured by picosecond fluorescence spectroscopy.'

H. Saito, W. Graudzus and E. O. Goebel, Springer Ser. Chem. Phys., (1982), 23, 353. 'Picosecond spectroscopy of highly excited gallium arsenide and cadmium sulfide.'

V. Sundstroem, T. Gillbro and H. Bergstroem, Springer Ser. Chem. Phys., (1982), 23, 242. 'Evidence for the existence of a short-lived twisted electronic state in triphenylmethane dyes.'

S. M. George, A. L. Harris, M. Berg and C. B. Harris, Springer Ser. Chem. Phys., (1982), 23, 196. 'The temperature dependence of homogeneous and inhomogeneous vibrational linewidth broadening studies using coherent picosecond Stokes scattering.'

M.L. Applebury and P.M. Rentzepis, Methods Enzymol., (1982), 81, 354. 'Picosecond spectroscopy of visual pigments'

G. Arjavalingam, A. Dienes and J.R. Whinnery, Opt. Lett., (1982), 5, 193. 'Highly synchronous mode-locked picosecond pulses at two wavelengths'

P. Bassler and U.K.A. Klein, J. Mol. Struct., (1982), 79, 113. 'Modification of rotational diffusion by an equilibrium reaction - a picosecond phasefluorimetric study of the excited state'

N.M. Lawandy, Appl. Phys. B, Photophys. and Laser Chem., (1982), 27,177. 'A new method of measuring ultra-short coherent light pulses'

R. Normandin and G.I. Stegeman, Appl. Phys. Lett., (1982), 40, 759. 'A picosecond transient digitizer based on nonlinear integrated optics'

C.V. Shank, R.L. Fork, R. Yen, R.H. Stolen and W.J. Tomlinson, Appl. Phys. Lett., (1982), 40, 761. 'Compression of femtosecond optical pulses'

L.B. Rubin and V.Z. Pashchenko, Eesti NSV Tead. Akad. Toim., Fuus., Mat., (1982), 2, 192. Chem. Abstr. 97-69518 'Picosecond fluorometry of exciton diffusion in the pigment apparatus of higher-plant chloroplasts'

C.V. Shank and B.I. Greene, Biol. Events Probed Ultrafast Laser Spectrosc., (1982), 417. Chem. Abstr. 97-123154 'Subpicosecond ultrafast laser technique - application and design'

M. Yamashita and T. Sato, Appl. Optics, (1982), 21, 2092. 'Picosecond gain spectroscopy of a laser dye during mode-locked laser action'

BIBLIOGRAPHY 1982

P. Valat, H. Tourbez and B. Alpert, Laser Chem., (1982), 1, 45.
'Electronic relaxation and oxygen recombination processes in
photodissociated oxyhemoglobin after picosecond flash photolysis.'

M. D. Fayer, Annu. Rev. Phys. Chem., (1982), 33, 63. 'Dynamics of
molecules in condensed phases : picosecond holographic grating
experiments.'

V. S. Antonov, E. V. Khoroshilova, N. P. Kuz'mina, V. S. Letokhov,
Y. A. Matveets, A. N. Shibanov and S. E. Egorov, Springer Ser.
Chem. Phys., (1982), 23, 310. 'Multiple photon processes in
molecules induced by picosecond ultraviolet laser pulses.'

J. W. Perry, E. A. Ryabov and A. H. Zewail, Laser Chem., (1982),
1, 9. 'Thermal lensing spectroscopy with picosecond pulse trains
and a new dual beam configuration.'

S. Meng, W. Zhang and Y. Kang, Jiguang, (1982), 9, 176; Chem.
Abstr. 98-081132. 'Superbroadening spectrum of picosecond pulses.'

R. Danielius and R. Rotomskis, Kvant. Elektron, (1982), 9, 1479;
Chem. Abstr. 98-108197. 'Measurement of kinetics of absorption
variations in poly(N-vinylcarbazole) : trinitroflourenone
complexes under picosecond excitation.'

V. Sundstroem, T. Gillbro and H. Bergstroem. Chem. Phys., (1982),
73, 439. 'Picosecond kinetics of radiationless relaxations of
triphenylmethane dyes. Evidence for a rapid excited-state
equilibrium between states of differing geometry.'

M. Bernstein, L. J. Rothberg and K. S. Peters, Chem. Phys.,
(1982), 23, 112. 'Picosecond time-resolved photoacoustic
spectroscopy.'

R. Danielius, A. Piskarskas and V. Sirutkaitis, Kvant. Elektron,
(1982), 9, 2491; Chem. Abstr. 98-116817. 'Picosecond optical
parametric oscillators and their use in kinetic absorption
spectroscopy.'

P. M. Rentzepis, Prog. Clin. Biol. Res., (1982), 102, 461.
'Biological applications of picosecond spectroscopy: on the early
picosecond intermediates of the visual chromophore - rhodopsin.'

B. Bareika, R. Danielius, G. Dikcius, G. Dadusa, A. Ishchenko, M.
A. Kudinova, A. Piskarskas, V. A. Sirutkaitis and A. I. Tolmachev,
Kvant. Elektron, (1982), 9, 2289; Chem. Abstr. 98-116679. 'Effect
of solvents on polymethine dye relaxation times in the picosecond
region.'

J. D. Spalink, M. L. Applebury, W. Sperling, A. H. Reynolds and P.
M. Rentzepis, Springer Ser. Chem. Phys., (1982), 23, 307.
'Picosecond studies of bacteriorhodopsin intermediates from 11-cis
rhodopsin and 9-cis rhodopsin.'

BIBLIOGRAPHY 1982

V. Sundstrom and T. Gillbro, J. Phys. Chem., (1982), 86, 1788. 'Viscosity-dependent isomerization yields of some cyanine dyes. A picosecond laser spectroscopy study'

M. Sumitani and K. Yoskihara, J. Chem. Phys., (1982), 76, 738. 'Chemisorption and reaction of cyclopropane on the (110) surface-trans-cis isomerization by two consecutive picosecond pulses'

N. Serpone, T. Netzel and M. Gouterman, J. Amer. Chem. Soc., (1982), 104, 246. 'A picosecond kinetic study of the excited-state properties of some osmium octaethyporphyrins'

M.W. Evans and C.J. Reid, Spectrochim. Acta, (1982), 38, 417. 'The evolution of molecular dynamics from picosecond to years'

A.V. Aleseev and U. K. Kopvillem, Spect. Lett., (1982), 15, 153. 'Towards attosecond spectroscopy'

G. Lockwood, J.J. McGarvey and R. Devonshire, Chem. Phys. Lett., (1982), 86, 123. 'Picosecond and nanosecond laser studies of intersystem crossing and excited state solvent substitution in dibromo-1, 2-bis(diphenylphosphinoethane) nickel (II)'

Y. Masumoto and S. Shinonoya, J. Phys. Soc. Jap., (1982), 51, 181. 'Dynamical relaxation processes: polaritons in CuCl studied by picosecond induced absorption'

H. Harde and H. Burggraf, Opt. Commun., (1982), 40, 441. 'Ultrahigh resolution coherence spectroscopy by means of periodic excitation with picosecond pulses'

L.J. Rothberg, N.J. Cooper, K.S. Peters and V. Vaida, J. Amer. Chem. Soc., (1982), 104, 3536. 'Picosecond dynamics of solution-phase photofragmentation of $Mn_2(CO)_{10}$

P.J. Thistlethwaite and P.J. Corkill, Chem. Phys. Lett., (1982), 85, 317. 'Direct observation of phototautomerism kinetics in 7-quinolinol by picosecond spectroscopy'

S.A. Akhmanov, R. Gadonas, R. Danielius, V.F. Kamalov, N.I. Koreteev, A.S. Piskarshas and Y.P. Svirko, Prog. Phys., (1982), 45, 481. 'Excited-state spectroscopy and picosecond relaxation at F centres'

T. Kobayashi and S. Nagakura, Biomembranes, (1982), 81, 368. 'Bleaching intermediate kinetics of rhodopsin - picosecond kinetics for squid rhodopsin'

J.A. Hutchinson, T.G. Traylor and L.J. Noe, J. Amer. Chem. Soc., (1982), 104, 3221. 'Picosecond study of the photodissociation of a model haemoprotein compared to haemoglobin'

Y. Wang, E.V. Sitzmann, F. Novak, C. Dupuy and K.B. Eisenthal, J. Amer. Chem. Soc., (1982), 104, 3238. 'Reaction of excited triplet diphenylcarbene studied with picosecond lasers'

268

W. Tsay and R. M. Hochstrasser, J. Chem. Educ., (1982), 59, 490.
'Picosecond spectroscopy in chemistry and biology.'

Y. Wang and K. B. Eisenthal, J. Chem. Educ., (1982), 59, 482.
'Picosecond laser studies of ultrafast processes in chemistry.'

D. H. Waldeck, W. T. Lotshaw, D. B. McDonald and G. R. Fleming,
Chem. Phys. Lett., (1982), 88, 297. 'Ultraviolet picosecond
pump-probe spectroscopy with a synchronously pumped dye laser.
Rotational diffusion of diphenyl butadiene.'

G. A. Kenny-Wallace and C. D. Jonah, J. Phys. Chem., (1982), 86,
2572. 'Picosecond spectroscopy and solvation clusters. The
dynamics of localizing electrons in polar fluids.'

J. A. Syage, W. R. Lambert, P. M. Felker, A. H. Zewail and R. M.
Hochstrasser, Chem. Phys. Lett., (1982), 88, 266. 'Picosecond
excitation and trans-cis isomerisation of stilbene in a supersonic
jet : Dynamics and spectra.'

M. W. Evans, J. Chem. Phys., (1982), 76, 5480. 'Molecular dynamics
simulation of liquid anisotropy. II. Rise and fall transients on a
picosecond time scale.'

A. Anialg, P. Saari, T. Tamm, K. Timpmann and A. M. Freiberg,
Kvant. Elektron, (1982), 9, 2449; Chem. Abstr. CA 98-116356.
'Spectrochronography of hot luminescence as a method for studying
picosecond relaxation in molecular systems.'

A. Anialg, K. Timpmann and A. Freiberg, Pis'ma Zh. Tekh. Fiz.,
(1982), 8, 1461; Chem. Abstr. 98-081244. 'Real time
spectrochronograph with temporary resolution better than 10 ps.'

D. F. Kelley, M. R. Mazur, P. M. Rentzepis and J. A. Berson, J.
Am. Chem. Soc., (1982), 104, 3764. 'Direct observation of a
hydrocarbon singlet 1,3-biradical by picosecond laser-induced
fluorescence spectrscopy.'

G. D. Patterson and P. J. Carrol, J. Chem. Phys., (1982), 76,
4356. 'Depolarised Rayleigh spectroscopy of small alkanes with
picosecond relaxation times.'

T. Okada, K. Kida and N. Mataga, Chem. Phys. Lett., (1982), 88,
157. 'Picosecond laser spectroscopy of photocycloaddition reaction
of 9-cyanoanthracene-1,3-diene systems and photodecomposition
reaction of the cycloadducts.'

C. A. Langhoff, B. Moore and M. DeMeuse, J. Am. Chem. Soc.,
(1982), 104, 3576. 'Diffusive and nondiffusive time scales in the
dissociation and recombination of molecular iodine in linear
alkanes.'

J. Baran, D. Elliott, P. A. Freedman, A. Grofcsik, M. Kubinyi and
W. J. Jones, J. Mol. Struct., (1982), 79, 109. 'Raman
amplification spectroscopy using picosecond lasers.'

W. Haehnel, J. A. Nairn, P. Reisberg and K. Sauer, Biochim.
Biophys. Acta., (1982), 680, 161. 'Picosecond fluorescence
kinetics and energy transfer in chloroplasts and algae.'

BIBLIOGRAPHY 1982

D. F. Voss, C. A. Paddock and R. B. Miles, Appl. Phys. Lett., (1982), 41, 51. 'Picosecond surface Raman spectroscopy beyond the damage limit.'

A. M. Freiberg, K. Timpmann, R. Tamkivi and R. Avarmaa, Eesti NSV Tead. Akad. Toim. Fuus. Mat., (1982), 31, 200; CA 97-052803. 'Study of the picosecond emission kinetics of chloroplast fragments using a synchronously pumped dye laser and spectrochronograph.'

J. C. Mialocq, E. Amouyal, A. Bernas and D. Grand, J. Phys. Chem., (1982), 86, 3173. 'Picosecond laser photolysis of aqueous indole and tryptophan.'

J. B. Clark, Diss. Abstr. Int. B, (1982), 42, 4437; Chem. Abstr., 97-81979. 'Picosecond spectroscopy of Rhodamine B.'

M. A. El-Sayed, C. L. Hsieh and M. Nicol, Springer Ser. Chem. Phys., (1982), 23, 302. 'Resonance Raman spectra of picosecond transients : application to bacteriorhodopsin.'

J. L. Martin, C. Poyart, A. Migus, Y. Lecarpentier, R. Astier and J. P. Chambaret, Springer Ser. Chem. Phys., (1982), 23, 294. 'Femtosecond and picosecond transient processes after photolysis of liganded heme proteins

M. J. McAuliffe, Diss. Abstr. Int. B, (1982), 43, 1506; Chem. Abstr. 98-063219. 'Picosecond laser studies of the photodissociation of diphenyldiazomethane, energy relaxation in o-hydroxybenzophenone and electron solvation.'

P. Bado, P. H. Berens, J. P. Bergsma, S. B. Wilson, K. R. Wilson and E. J. Heller, Springer Ser. Chem. Phys., (1982), 23, 260. 'Picosecond dynamics of diatomic iodine photodissociation.'

G. W. Scott, Sci. Tech. Aerosp. Rep., (1982), 20; Chem. Abstr. 98-090387. 'Picosecond flash spectroscopic studies on ultraviolet stabilizers and stabilized polymers.'

P. Bado, P. H. Berens, J. P. Bergsma, S. B. Wilson and K. R. Wilson, Gov. Rep. Announce. Index(U.S.), (1982), 82, 4842; Chem. Abstr. 98-044049. 'Picosecond dynamics of molecular iodine photodissociation.'

R. C. Sharp, Diss. Abstr. Int. B, (1982), 43, 1531; Chem. Abstr. 98-062323. 'Picosecond time resolved infrared double resonance studies of sulfurhexafluoride and pentafluorobenzene.'

P. Bassler and U.K.A. Klein, J. Mol. Struct., (1982), 79, 113. 'Modification of rotational diffusion by an equilibrium reaction – a picosecond phasefluorimetric study of the excited state'

N.M. Lawandy, Appl. Phys. B: Photophys. and Laser Chem., (1982), 27, 177. 'A new method of measuring ultra-short coherent light pulses'

BIBLIOGRAPHY 1982

H. Nakata and E. Otsuka, Appl. Phys. B: Photophys. and Laser Chem., (1982), 27, 207. 'Multichannel time-resolved measurement in far-infrared magnetoabsorption'

R. Normandin and G.I. Stegeman, Appl. Phys. Lett., (1982), 40, 759. 'A picosecond transient digitizer based on nonlinear integrated optics'

C.V. Shank, R.L. Fork, R. Yen, R.H. Stolen and W.J. Tomlinson, Appl. Phys. Lett., (1982), 40, 761. 'Compression of femtosecond optical pulses'

L.B. Rubin and V.Z. Pashchenko, Eesti NSV Tead. Akad. Toim., Fuus., Mat., (1982), 2, 192; Chem. Abstr. 97-69518. 'Picosecond fluorometry of exciton diffusion in the pigment apparatus of higher-plant chloroplasts'

C.V. Shank and B.I. Greene, Biol. Events Probed Ultrafast Laser Spectrosc., (1982), 417; Chem. Abstr. 97-123154. 'Subpicosecond ultrafast laser technique - application and design'

M. Yamashita and T. Sato, Appl. Optics, (1982), 21, 2092. 'Picosecond gain spectroscopy of a laser dye during mode-locked laser action'

J. Baran, D. Elliott, P.A. Freedman, A. Grofscik, M. Kubinyi and W.J. Jones, J. Mol. Struct., (1982), 79, 109. 'Raman amplification spectroscopy using picosecond lasers'

J. Terner, D.F. Voss, C. Paddock, R.B. Miles and T.G. Spiro, J. Phys. Chem., (1982), 86, 859. 'Picosecond resonance spectrum of the oxyhaemoglobin photoproduct'

BIBLIOGRAPHY 1981

G. J. Zaal, Esc. Opt. Cauntica, (1981), 3, 165; Chem. Abstr. 98-188144. 'Picosecond light pulses and their detection.'

A. G. Doukas, F. Pellegrino, D. Wong, V. Stefancic, J. Buchert, R. R. Alfano and B. A. Zilinskas, Photosynth. Proc. Int. Congr., (1981), 1, 59; Chem. Abstr. 97-52714. 'Picosecond absorption and fluorescence studies of the isolated phycobiliproteins from the blue-green alga Nostoc sp'.

J. Pantoflicek, R. Danielius and R. Gadonas, Konf. Cesk. Fyz., (1981), 1, 2; Chem. Abstr. 97-20888. 'Picosecond spectroscopy of chlorophyll a in polystyrene foil.',

H-J. Hartmann and A. Laubereau, Appl. Optics, (1981), 20, 4259. 'Sensitive detection of IR photons with picosecond time resolution'

F. Heisel, J.A. Miehe and B. Sipp, Nuovo Cimento Soc. Ital. Fis. B, (1981), 1, 221; Chem. Abstr. 95-70706. 'Applications of synchronously pumped and cavity-dumped dye laser associated with streak camera operated at the repetitive mode to time-resolved spectroscopy'

T. Kushida, S. Kinoshita, I. Tanaka, Y. Kinoshita and S. Kimura, J. Lumin., (1981), 2, 787. 'Picosecond fluorescence spectroscopy of dye molecules in living biological cells'

D. Rosen, A.G. Doukas, Y. Budansky, A. Katz and R.R. Alfano, IEEE J. Quantum Elect., (1981), 17, 2264. 'A subpicosecond tunable ring dye laser and its applications to time-resolved fluorescence spectroscopy'

G.R. Fleming, D. Waldeck and G.S. Beddard, Nuovo Cimento Soc. Ital. Fis. B, (1981), 63B, 151. 'Applications of synchronously pumped dye lasers to time-resolved emission and absorption spectroscopy'

G.A. Kenney-Wallace, Adv. Chem. Phys., (1981), 47, 535. 'Picosecond spectroscopy and dynamics of electron relaxation processes in liquids'

F. Heisel, J.A. Miehe and B. Sipp, Rev. Sci. Instrum., (1981), 52, 992. 'Characteristics and performances of a streak camera operating in repetitive mode'

S.N. Ketkar, J.W. Keto and C.H. Holder, Rev. Sci. Instrum., (1981), 52, 405. 'A rapid scanning auto-correlation scheme for continuous monitoring of picosecond laser pulses'

S. Kinoshita, H. Ohta and T. Kushida, Rev. Sci. Instrum., (1981), 52, 572. 'Subnanosecond fluorescence lifetime measuring system using single-photon counting method with mode-locked laser excitation'

M. Bridoux, A. Deffontaine, M. Delhaye, B. Rose and E. da Silva, J. Raman Spectrosc., (1981), 6, 515. 'Picosecond multichannel Raman spectroscopy of solids'

BIBLIOGRAPHY 1981

R.R. Bucks, T.L. Netzel, I. Fujita and S.G. Boxer, J. Phys. Chem., (1981), 86, 1947. 'Picosecond spectroscopic study of chlorophyll-based models for the primary photochemistry of photosynthesis'

Z. Vardeny and J. Tauc, Opt. Commun., (1981), 39, 396. 'Picosecond coherence coupling in the pump and probe technique'

Y. Wang, M. McAuliffe, F. Novak and K.B. Eisenthal, J. Phys. Chem., (1981), 85, 3736. 'Picosecond dynamics of twisted internal charge-transfer phenomena'

D. Huppert, S.D. Rand, P.M. Rentzepis, P.F. Barbara, W.S. Struve and Z.R. Grabowski, J. Chem. Phys., (1981), 75, 5714. 'Picosecond kinetics of p-dimethylaminobenzonitrile'

W.R. Lambert, P.M. Felker and A.H. Zewail, J. Chem. Phys., (1981), 75, 5958. 'Quantum beats and dephasing in isolated large molecules cooled by supersonic jet expansion and excited by picosecond pulses: anthracene'

Y. Liang, D.K. Negus, R.M. Hochstrasser, M. Gunner and P.L. Dutton, Chem. Phys. Lett., (1981), 84, 236. 'Picosecond kinetic absorption studies of an iron porphyrin and bacteriochlorophyll using a streak camera'

M. Migita, T. Okada, N. Mataga, S. Nishitani, N. Kurata, Y. Sakata and S. Misumi, Chem. Phys. Lett., (1981), 84, 263. 'Picosecond time-resolved observation of photo-induced charge separation from the singlet excited state of porphyrin-quinone model systems'

A.G. Doukas, V. Stefancic, J. Buchert, R.R. Alfano and B.A. Zilinskas, Photochem. Photobiol., (1981), 34, 505. 'Exciton annihilation in the isolated phycobiliproteins from the blue-green alga Nostoc. sp. using picosecond absorption spectroscopy'

K. Kamogawa, A. Namiki, N. Nakashima, K. Yoshihara and I. Ikegami, Photochem. Photobiol., (1981), 34, 511. 'Picosecond transient behaviour of reaction-centre particles of photosystem I isolated from spinach chloroplasts. Energy and electron transfer upon single multiple photon excitation'

J.D. Simon and K.S Peters, J. Amer. Chem. Soc., (1981), 103, 6403. 'Solvent effects on the picosecond dynamics of the photoreduction of benzophenone by aromatic amines'

P.A. Cornelius, A.W. Steele, D.A. Chernoff and R.M. Hochstrasser, Proc. Nat. Acad. Sci. US-Bio., (1981), 78, 7526. 'Different dissociation pathways and observations of an excited deoxy state in picosecond photolysis of oxymyoglobin and carboxymyoglobin'

P.A. Cornelius, A.W. Stelle, D.A. Chernoff and R.M. Hochstrasser, Chem. Phys. Lett., (1981), 82, 9. 'The observation of a picosecond transient in the relaxation of an iron porphyrin'

S.A. Krysanov and M.V. Alfimov, Chem. Phys. Lett., (1981), 82, 51. 'Cis-trans photoisomerization of thioindigoid dyes studied by picosecond flash photolysis'

BIBLIOGRAPHY 1981

P.G. May, W. Sibbett, J.R. Taylor, Febs. Lett., (1981), 134, 240. 'Picosecond relaxation of the fluorescence probes ANS and TNS in aqueous solutions'

S.S. Brody, J. Barber, C. Tredwell and G. Beddard, Z. Naturforsch. Sect., (1981), 36, 1021. 'Effects of linolenic acid on the spectra properties and picosecond fluorescence of pea chloroplasts'

D. Huppert and E. Kolodney, Chem. Phys., (1981), 63, 401. 'Picosecond proton transfer studies in water-alcohol solutions'

U. Mayer, H. Autweter, A. Braun, H.C. Wolf and D. Schmidt, Chem. Phys., (1981), 59, 449. 'Investigation of the excimer dynamics in 9, 10-dichloroanthracene crystals using picosecond spectroscopy'

A.A. Oraevsky, A.V. Sharkov and D.N. Nikogosyan, Chem. Phys, Lett., (1981), 83, 276. 'Picosecond study of electronically excited singlet states of nucleic acid components'

P.Hering, A.G.M. Maaswinkel and K.L. Kompa, Chem. Phys. Lett., (1981), 83, 222. 'Picosecond UV laser-induced multiphoton ionization and fragmentation of benzene'

V. Sundstrom and T. Gillbro, Chem. Phys., (1981), 61, 257. 'Viscosity dependent radiationless relaxation rate of cyanine dyes. A picosecond laser spectroscopy study'

V.S. Chirvonyi, B.M. Dzhagarov, A.M. Shulga and G.P. Gurinovich, Dokl. Akad. Nauk. SSSR., (1981), 259, 1256. 'Picosecond spectroscopy of porphyrin complexes with Ni(II). Excited electronic states and axial ligand photodissociation'

A. Antonetti, R. Astier, J.L. Martin, A. Migus, D. Hulin and A. Mysyrowicz, Opt. Commun., (1981), 38, 431. 'Picosecond spectroscopy in Cu_2O: exciton dynamics and 2-photon absorption'

J.L. Ferrier, A. Planner and G. Rivoire, Acta Phys. Pol., (1981), 60, 241. 'Measurement of linewidth in stimulated Raman scattering under picosecond pumping '

D. Straub, P.M. Rentzepis and D. Huppert, J. Photochem., (1981), 17, 419. 'Picosecond spectroscopy of some metalloporphyrins'

R.L. Pineault, C.G. Morgante and W.S. Struve, J. Photochem., (1981), 17, 435. 'Picosecond triplet state dynamics and photodissociation in 2- and 9-iodoanthracene'

E. Heumann, Z. Naturforsch., (1981), 36, 1323. 'Determinisation of diffusion parameters of solvated molecules by measuring the relaxation kinetics on the picosecond time scale'

G.S. Beddard, T. Doust and J. Hudales, Nature, (1981), 294, 145. 'Structural features in ethanol-water mixtures revealed by picosecond fluorescence anisotropy'

S.K. Rentsch, R.V. Danielius and R.A. Gadonas, Chem. Phys. Lett., (1981), 84, 450. 'Picosecond time-resolved kinetic studies on the formation of short-lived pseudoisocyanine iodide photo-isomers in methanol and ethylene glycol'

BIBLIOGRAPHY 1981/1980

G.G. Gurzadyan, D.N. Nikogosyan and A.A. Belogurov, Biofizika SSSR, (1981), 26, 991. 'Photochemical stability of aromatic amino acids under picosecond laser UV radiation'

M.A.J. Rogers, J. Phys. Chem., (1981), 85, 3372. 'Picosecond fluorescence studies of xanthene dyes in anionic micelles in water and reverse micelles in heptane'

S.Y. Hou, C.P. Dupuy, M.J. McAuliffe, D.A. Horovat and K.B. Eisenthal, J. Amer. Chem. Soc., (1981), 103, 6982. 'Picosecond laser study of the adiabatic photodissociation of an endoperoxide'

F. Pellegrino, D. Wong, R.R. Alfano and B.A. Zilinskas, Photochem. Photobiol., (1981), 34, 691. 'Fluorescence relaxation kinetics and quantum yield from phycobilisomes of the blue-green alga Nostac sp. measured as a function of single picosecond pulse intensity'

M-M. Cordonnier, P. Mathis and L.H. Pratt, Photochem. Photobiol., (1981), 34, 733. 'Phototransformation kinetics of undegraded oat and pea phytochrome initiated by laser flash excitation of the red-absorbing form'

M.C. Adams, D.J. Bradley, W. Sibbett and J.R. Taylor, J. Mol. Struct., (1980), 61, 5. 'Application of the Synchroscan streak camera to real time picosecond measurements of molecular energy transfer'

J.M. Harris, W.T. Barnes, T.L. Gustafson, T.H. Bushaw and F.E. Lytle, Rev. Sci. Instrum., (1980), 51, 988. 'Simple, inexpensive photodetector for subnanosecond sources'

P.S. Mak, C.C. Davis, B.J. Foster and C.H. Lee, Rev. Sci. Instrum., (1980), 51, 647. 'Measurement of picosecond light pulses with a two-photon photo-conductivity detector'

D.J. Bradley, S.F. Bryant and W. Sibbett, Rev. Sci. Instrum., (1980), 51, 824. 'Intensity dependent time resolution and dynamic range of photochron picosecond streak cameras. II. Linear photoelectric recording'

BIBLIOGRAPHY 1975-1979

K.P. Ghiggino, A.J. Roberts and D. Phillips, Springer-Verlag Ser. Chem. Phys., (1979), 6, 98. 'Time-resolved fluorescence spectroscopy using pulsed laser excitation'

M.R. Topp, Appl. Spectroscopy Rev., (1979), 14, 1. 'Pulsed laser spectroscopy'

J.C. Gauthier and J.F Delpech, Adv. Electron. and Electron Phys., (1978), 46, 131. 'Time-resolved laser fluorescence spectroscopy for atomic and molecular excited states: kinetic studies'

E.P. Ippen and C.V. Shank, Physics Today, (1978), 31, 41. 'Sub-picosecond spectroscopy'

D. Holten and M.W. Windsor, Ann. Rev. Biophys. Bioeng., (1978), 7, 189. 'Picosecond flash photolysis in biology and biophysics'

K.G. Spears, L.E. Cramer and L.D. Hoffland, Rev. Sci. Instrum., (1978), 49, 255. 'Subnanosecond time-resolved photon counting with tunable lasers'

R.L. Fork and F.A. Beisser, Appl. Optics, (1978), 17, 3534. 'Real-time intensity autocorrelation interferometer'

S. Weiss, J. Chem. Phys., (1978), 67, 5735. 'Subpicosecond lifetimes by infrared line broadening measurements'

G.R. Fleming and G.S. Beddard, Optics and Laser Technology, (Oct. 1978), 257. 'CW mode-locked dye lasers for ultrafast spectroscopic studies'

'Picosecond Phenomena' Edited by C.V. Shank, E.P.Ippen and S.L. Shapiro, (1978), Springer-Verlag.

'Lasers in Chemistry', edited by M.A. West, (1977), Elsevier.

'Ultrashort light pulses. Picosecond Techniques and Applications' Edited by S.L. Shapiro, (1977), Springer-Verlag.

A. Laudereau and W. Kaiser in 'Chemical and Biological Applications of Lasers', vol. 2, (1976), Edited by C.B. Moore, Academic Press

M.A. West in 'Creation and Detection of the Excited State', (1976), edited by W.R. Ware, Dekker (New York).

R.R. Alfano and S.L. Shapiro, Physics Today, (1975), 28, 30. M.M. Malley in 'Creation and Detection of the Excited State', vol. 2, (1974), Edited by W.R. Ware, Dekker. (Picosecond techniques)

H. Mahr and M.D. Hirsch, Optics Comm., (1975), 13, 96. (Method for measuring picosecond phenomena in photolabile species using upconversion)